Masterpieces of
Humor

Compiled by Rosamund Morris

Hart Publishing Company, • New York

ACKNOWLEDGMENTS

Grateful acknowledgment is made to the copyright owners for permission to reprint the following stories:

"The Mouse" by Saki (H. H. Munro) from *The Short Stories of Saki;* copyright 1930, 1957 by The Viking Press, Inc., reprinted by kind permission of The Viking Press, Inc., and The Bodley Head Ltd.

"Chicago Safari" by Hannibal Coons; copyright 1951 by Hannibal Coons, reprinted by kind permission of Brandt & Brandt.

"A Piece of Pie" from *Take It Easy* by Damon Runyon; copyright 1937 by Damon Runyon, reprinted by kind permission of Damon Runyon, Jr.

"Hold 'Em Yale" by Damon Runyon; copyright 1931 by P. F. Collier & Son Co., reprinted by kind permission of Damon Runyon, Jr.

"Statement of James Wentworth, B.A." from *The Vexations of A. J. Wentworth, B.A.* by H. E. Ellis; copyright 1950 by H. E. Ellis, reprinted by kind permission of Curtis Brown Ltd., London, England.

"You Could Look It Up" from *My World—and Welcome to It* by James Thurber, published by Harcourt, Brace & World, Inc.; copyright 1942 by James Thurber, reprinted by kind permission of Mrs. James Thurber.

"The Skipper's Pink Panties" from *All The Ships at Sea* by William J. Lederer; copyright 1950 by William J. Lederer, reprinted by kind permission of William Sloane Associates.

"Little Bit and the America" from *Father. Dear Father* by Ludwig Bemelmans; copyright 1953 by Ludwig Bemelmans, reprinted by kind permission of The Viking Press, Inc.

"Love Is A Fallacy" from the book *The Many Loves of Dobie Gillis* by Max Shulman; copyright 1951 by Max Shulman, reprinted by kind permission of Doubleday & Company, Inc.

"The Mock Governor" copyright 1948 by Max Shulman from *The Many Loves of Dobie Gillis* by Max Shulman, reprinted by kind permission of Doubleday & Company, Inc.

"Mr. Kaplan and Vocabulary" from *The Education of Hyman Kaplan* by Leonard Q. Ross; copyright 1937 by Harcourt, Brace & World, Inc., reprinted by kind permission of Harcourt, Brace & World, Inc.

"You Were Perfectly Fine" from *The Portable Dorothy Parker;* copyright 1929, 1957 by Dorothy Parker; originally appeared in The New Yorker, reprinted by kind permission of The Viking Press, Inc.

CONTENTS

ELLIS PARKER BUTLER (1869-1937)

... was a prolific humorist, turning out a steady stream of stories and essays for over forty years. He came from a poor, but well-read Iowa family. Though he was able to complete only one year of high school, he was encouraged from childhood in his liking for literature. Mark Twain lived for a while in Butler's home town, and he too influenced the boy's writing.

Butler's reputation rests almost exclusively on one story, "Pigs Is Pigs." Published in 1905, this slight, but hilarious tale of a railway agent beleaguered by guinea-pigs was an immediate success; it is considered a classic of American farce.

Rules is rules,

said the railway agent, and

PIGS IS PIGS

MIKE FLANNERY, the Westcote agent of the Inter-urban Express Company, leaned over the counter of the express office and shook his fist. Mr. Morehouse, angry and red, stood on the other side of the counter, trembling with rage. The argument had been long and heated, and at last Mr. Morehouse had talked himself speechless. The cause of the trouble stood on the counter between the two men. It was a soap box across the top of which were nailed a number of strips, form-ing a rough but serviceable cage. In it two spotted guinea-pigs were greedily eating lettuce leaves.

"Do as you like, then!" shouted Flannery, "pay for them and take them, or don't pay for them and leave them be. Rules is rules, Mister Morehouse, and Mike

Flannery's not going to be called down for breaking them."

"But, you everlastingly stupid idiot!" shouted Mr. Morehouse, madly shaking a flimsy printed book beneath the agent's nose, "can't you read it here—in your own plain printed rates? 'Pets, domestic, Franklin to Westcote, if properly boxed, twenty-five cents each.' " He threw the book on the counter in disgust. "What more do you want? Aren't they pets? Aren't they domestic? Aren't they properly boxed? What?"

He turned and walked back and forth rapidly, frowning ferociously.

Suddenly he turned to Flannery and, forcing his voice to an artificial calmness, spoke slowly but with intense sarcasm.

"Pets," he said. "P-e-t-s! Twenty-five cents each. There are two of them. One! Two! Two times twenty-five are fifty! Can you understand that? I offer you fifty cents."

Flannery reached for the book. He ran his hand through the pages and stopped at page sixty-four.

"And I don't take fifty cents," he whispered in mockery. "Here's the rule for it. 'When the agent be in any doubt regarding which of two rates applies to a shipment, he shall charge the larger. The consignee may file a claim for the overcharge.' In this case, Mister Morehouse, I be in doubt. Pets them animals may be, and domestic they are, but pigs I'm blame sure they are, and my rules say plain as the nose on your face, 'Pigs, Franklin to Westcote, thirty cents each.' And,

Mr. Morehouse, by my arithmetical knowledge two times thirty comes to sixty cents."

Mr. Morehouse shook his head savagely. "Nonsense!" he shouted, "confounded nonsense, I tell you! Why, you poor ignorant foreigner, that rule means common pigs, domestic pigs, not guinea-pigs!"

Flannery was stubborn.

"Pigs is pigs," he declared firmly. "Guinea-pigs or Irish pigs is all the same to the Interurban Express Company and to Mike Flannery. The nationality of the pig creates no differential in the rate, Mister Morehouse! It would be the same if they were Dutch pigs or Russian pigs. Mike Flannery," he added, "is here to tend to the express business and not to hold conversation with pigs in seventeen languages for to discover if they're Chinese or Tipperary by birth and nativity."

Mr. Morehouse hesitated and then flung out his arms wildly.

"Very well!" he shouted, "you shall hear of this! Your president shall hear of this! It is an outrage! I have offered you fifty cents. You refuse it! Keep the pigs until you are ready to take the fifty cents, but, by George, sir, if one hair of those pigs' heads is harmed, I will have the law on you!"

He turned and stalked out, slamming the door. Flannery carefully lifted the soap box from the counter and placed it in a corner. He was not worried. He felt the peace that comes to a faithful servant who has done his duty and done it well.

Mr. Morehouse went home raging. His boy, who

had been awaiting the guinea-pigs, knew better than to ask him for them. He was a normal boy and therefore always had a guilty conscience when his father was angry. So the boy slipped quietly around the house. There is nothing so soothing to a guilty conscience as to be out of the path of the avenger.

Mr. Morehouse stormed into the house. "Where's the ink?" he shouted at his wife as soon as his foot was across the doorsill.

Mrs. Morehouse jumped, guiltily. She never used ink. She had not seen the ink, nor moved the ink, nor thought of the ink, but her husband's tone convicted her of the guilt of having borne and reared a boy, and she knew that whenever her husband wanted anything in a loud voice, the boy had been at it.

"I'll find Sammy," she said meekly.

When the ink was found, Mr. Morehouse wrote rapidly, and he read the completed letter and smiled a triumphant smile.

"That will settle that crazy Irishman!" he exclaimed. "When they get that letter, he will hunt another job, all right!"

A week later Mr. Morehouse received a long official envelope with the card of the Interurban Express Company in the upper left corner. He tore it open eagerly and drew out a sheet of paper. At the top it bore the number A6754. The letter was short. "Subject—Rate on guinea-pigs," it said, "Dr. Sir—We are in receipt of your letter regarding rate on guinea-pigs between Franklin and Westcote, addressed to the president of this company. All claims for overcharge should be addressed to the Claims Department."

Mr. Morehouse wrote the Claims Department. He wrote six pages of choice sarcasm, vituperation, and argument, and sent them to Claims.

A few weeks later he received a reply from the Claims Department. Attached to it was his last letter.

"Dr. Sir," said the reply. "Your letter of the 16th inst., addressed to this Department, subject rate on guinea-pigs from Franklin to Westcote, rec'd. We have taken up the matter with our agent at Westcote, and his reply is attached herewith. He informs us that you refused to receive the consignment or to pay the charges. You have therefore no claim against this company, and your letter regarding the proper rate on the consignment should be addressed to our Tariff Department."

Mr. Morehouse wrote to the Tariff Department. He stated his case clearly and gave his arguments in full, quoting a page or two from the encyclopedia to prove that guinea-pigs were not common pigs.

With the care that characterizes corporations when they are systematically conducted, Mr. Morehouse's letter was numbered, O.K.'d, and started through the regular channels. Duplicate copies of the bill of lading, manifest, Flannery's receipt for the package, and several other pertinent papers were pinned to the letter, and they were passed to the head of the Tariff Department.

The head of the Tariff Department put his feet on

his desk and yawned. He looked through the papers carelessly.

"Miss Kane," he said to his stenographer, "take this letter. 'Agent, Westcote, N.J. Please advise why consignment referred to in attached papers was refused domestic pet rates.' "

Miss Kane made a series of curves and angles on her notebook and waited with pencil poised. The department head looked at the papers again.

"Huh! guinea-pigs!" he said. "Probably starved to death by this time! Add this to that letter: 'Give condition of consignment at present.' "

He tossed the papers on the stenographer's desk, took his feet from his own desk, and went out to lunch.

When Mike Flannery received the letter he scratched his head.

"Give present condition," he repeated thoughtfully. "Now what do them clerks be wanting to know, I wonder! 'Present condition,' is it? Them pigs, praise St. Patrick, are in good health, so far as I know, but I never was no veterinary surgeon to pigs. Maybe them clerks want me to call in the pig doctor and have their pulses taken. One thing I do know, however, which is they've glorious appetites for pigs their size. Eats? They'd eat the brass padlocks off of a barn door! If the paddy pig, by the same token, ate as hearty as these pigs do, there'd be a famine in Ireland."

To assure himself that his report would be up to date, Flannery went to the rear of the office and looked into the cage. The pigs had been transferred to a larger box—a dry goods box.

"One,— two,— three,— four,— five,— six,— seven,— eight!" he counted. "Seven spotted and one all black. All well and hearty and all eating like raging hippopotamuses." He went back to his desk and wrote.

"Mr. Morgan, Head of Tariff Department," he wrote. "Why do I say guinea-pigs is pigs because they is pigs and will be 'til you say they ain't which is what the rule book says stop your jollying me you know it as well as I do. As to health they are all well and hoping you are the same. P.S. There are eight now the family increased all good eaters. P.S. I paid out so far two dollars for cabbage which they like shall I put in bill for same what?"

Morgan, head of the Tariff Department, when he received this letter, laughed. He read it again and became serious. He looked up and thought it over.

"By George!" he said, "Flannery is right, 'pigs is pigs.' I'll have to get authority on this thing. Meanwhile, Miss Kane, take this letter: Agent, Westcote, N.J. Regarding shipment guinea-pigs, File No. A6754. Rule 83, General Instructions to Agents, clearly states that agents shall collect from consignee all costs of provender, etc., etc., required for live stock while in transit or storage. You will proceed to collect same from consignee."

Flannery received this letter next morning, and when he read it he grinned.

"Proceed to collect," he said softly. "How them clerks do like to be talking! *Me* proceed to collect two dollars and twenty-five cents off Mister Morehouse! I wonder do them clerks *know* Mister Morehouse? I'll get it! Oh, yes! 'Mister Morehouse, two and a quarter, please.' 'Certainly, my dear friend Flannery. Delighted!' *Not!*"

Flannery drove the express wagon to Mr. Morehouse's door. Mr. Morehouse answered the bell.

"Ah, ha!" he cried as soon as he saw it was Flannery. "So you've come to your senses at last, have you? I thought you would! Bring the box in."

"I have no box," said Flannery coldly. "I have a bill against Mister John C. Morehouse for two dollars and twenty-five cents for cabbages eaten by his pigs. Would you wish to pay it?"

"Pay—Cabbages—!" gasped Mr. Morehouse. "Do you mean to say that two little guinea-pigs—"

"Eight!" said Flannery. "Papa and mamma and the six children. Eight!"

For answer Mr. Morehouse slammed the door in Flannery's face. Flannery looked at the door reproachfully.

"I take it the consignee don't want to pay for them cabbages," he said. "If I know signs of refusal, the consignee refuses to pay for one dang cabbage leaf and be hanged to me!"

Mr. Morgan, head of the Tariff Department, consulted the president of the Interurban Express Company regarding guinea-pigs, as to whether they were pigs or not pigs. The president was inclined to treat the matter lightly.

"What is the rate on pigs and on pets?" he asked.

"Pigs thirty cents, pets twenty-five," said Morgan.

"Then of course guinea-pigs are pigs," said the president.

"Yes," agreed Morgan, "I look at it that way, too. A thing that can come under two rates is naturally to be classed as the higher. But are guinea-pigs, pigs? Aren't they rabbits?"

"Come to think of it," said the president, "I believe they are more like rabbits. Sort of half-way station between pig and rabbit. I think the question is this—are guinea-pigs of the domestic pig family? I'll ask Professor Gordon. He is an authority on such things. Leave the papers with me."

The president put the papers on his desk and wrote a letter to Professor Gordon. Unfortunately the Professor was in South America collecting zoological specimens, and the letter was forwarded to him by his wife. As the Professor was in the highest Andes, where no white man had ever penetrated, the letter was many months in reaching him. The president forgot the guinea-pigs, Morgan forgot them, Mr. Morehouse forgot them, but Flannery did not. One-half of his time he gave to the duties of his agency; the other half was devoted to the guinea-pigs. Long before Professor Gordon received the president's letter, Morgan received one from Flannery.

"About them guinea-pigs," it said, "what shall I do they are great in family life, no race suicide for them, there are thirty-two now shall I sell them do you take this express office for a menagerie, answer quick."

Morgan reached for a telegraph blank and wrote:

"Agent, Westcote. Don't sell pigs."

He then wrote Flannery a letter calling his attention to the fact that the pigs were not the property of the company but were merely being held during a settlement of a dispute regarding rates. He advised Flannery to take the best possible care of them.

Flannery, letter in hand, looked at the pigs and sighed. The dry goods box cage had become too small. He boarded up twenty feet of the rear of the express office to make a large and airy home for them, and went about his business. He worked with feverish intensity when out on his rounds, for the pigs required attention and took most of his time. Some months later, in desperation, he seized a sheet of paper and wrote "160" across it and mailed it to Morgan. Morgan returned it asking for explanation. Flannery replied:

"There are now one hundred sixty of them pigs, for heavens sake let me sell off some, do you want me to go crazy, what."

"Sell no pigs," Morgan wired.

Not long after this the president of the express company received a letter from Professor Gordon. It was a long and scholarly letter, but the point was that the guinea-pig was the *Cavia aparoea* while the common pig was the genus *Sus* of the family *Suidae*. He remarked that they were prolific and multiplied rapidly.

"They are not pigs," said the president, decidedly, to Morgan. "The twenty-five cent rate applies."

Morgan made the proper notation on the papers that
had accumulated in File A6754 and turned them over
to the Audit Department. The Audit Department took
some time to look the matter up and, after the usual
delay, wrote Flannery that as he had on hand one
hundred and sixty guinea-pigs, the property of consignee, he should deliver them and collect charges at
the rate of twenty-five cents each.

Flannery spent a day herding his charges through a
narrow opening in their cage so that he might count
them.

"Audit Dept." He wrote, when he had finished the
count, "you are way off there may be was one hundred
and sixty guinea-pigs once, but wake up don't be a
back number. I've got even eight hundred, now shall
I collect for eight hundred or what, how about sixty-
four dollars I paid out for cabbages."

It required a great many letters back and forth before the Audit Department was able to understand why
the error had been made of billing one hundred and
sixty instead of eight hundred, and still more time for
it to get the meaning of the "cabbages."

Flannery was crowded into a few feet at the extreme
front of the office. The pigs had all the rest of the room
and two boys were employed constantly attending to
them. The day after Flannery had counted the guinea-
pigs there were eight more added to his drove, and by
the time the Audit Department gave him authority to
collect for eight hundred Flannery had given up all
attempts to attend to the receipts of the delivery of

goods. He was hastily building galleries around the express office, tier above tier. He had four thousand and sixty-four guinea-pigs to care for. More were arriving daily.

Immediately following its authorization the Audit Department sent another letter, but Flannery was too busy to open it. They wrote another and then they telegraphed:

"Error in guinea-pig bill. Collect for two guinea-pigs, fifty cents. Deliver all to consignee."

Flannery read the telegram and cheered up. He wrote out a bill as rapidly as his pencil could travel over the paper and ran all the way to the Morehouse home. At the gate he stopped suddenly. The house stared at him with vacant eyes. The windows were bare of curtains, and he could see into the empty rooms. A sign on the porch said, "To Let." Mr. Morehouse had moved. Flannery ran all the way back to the express office. Sixty-nine guinea-pigs had been born during his absence. He ran out again and made feverish inquiries in the village. Mr. Morehouse had not only moved, but he had left Westcote. Flannery returned to the express office and found that two hundred and six guinea-pigs had entered the world since he left. He wrote a telegram to the Audit Department.

"Can't collect fifty cents for two guinea-pigs consignee has left town address unknown what shall I do? Flannery."

The telegram was handed to one of the clerks in the Audit Department, and as he read it he laughed.

"Flannery must be crazy. He ought to know that the thing to do is to return the consignment here," said the clerk. He telegraphed Flannery to send the pigs to the main office of the company at Franklin.

When Flannery received the telegram, he set to work. The six boys he had engaged to help him also set to work. They worked with the haste of desperate men, making cages out of soap boxes, cracker boxes, and all kinds of boxes, and as fast as the cages were completed, they filled them with guinea-pigs and expressed them to Franklin. Day after day the cages of guinea-pigs flowed in a steady stream from Westcote to Franklin, and still Flannery and his six helpers ripped and nailed and packed—relentlessly and feverishly. At the end of the week they had shipped two hundred and eighty cases of guinea-pigs, and there were in the express office seven hundred and four more pigs than when they began packing them.

"Stop sending pigs. Warehouse full," came a telegram to Flannery. He stopped packing only long enough to wire back, "Can't stop," and kept on sending them. On the next train up from Franklin came one of the company's inspectors. He had instructions to stop the stream of guinea-pigs at all hazards. As his train drew up at Westcote station, he saw a cattle-car standing on the express company's siding. When he reached the express office he saw the express wagon backed up to the door. Six boys were carrying bushel baskets full of guinea-pigs from the office and dumping them into the wagon. Inside the room Flannery, with his coat and vest off, was shoveling guinea-pigs into bushel baskets with a coal scoop. He was winding up the guinea-pig episode for once and for all.

He looked up at the inspector with a snort of anger.

"One wagonload more and I'll be quit of them, and never will you catch Flannery with no more foreign pigs on his hands. No, sir! They near was the death of me. Next time I'll know that pigs of whatever nationality is domestic pets—and go at the lowest rate."

He began shoveling again rapidly, speaking quickly between breaths.

"Rules may be rules, but you can't fool Mike Flannery twice with the same trick—when it comes to live stock, dang the rules. So long as Flannery runs this express office—pigs is pets—and cows is pets—and horses is pets—and lions and tigers and Rocky Mountain goats is pets—and the rate on them is twenty-five cents."

He paused long enough to let one of the boys put an empty basket in the place of the one he had just filled. There were only a few guinea-pigs left. As he noted their limited number, his natural habit of looking on the bright side returned.

"Well, anyhow," he said cheerfully, "it's not so bad as it might be. What if them guinea-pigs had been elephants!"

SAKI (1870-1916)

. . . took his pen name from "The Rubaiyat of Omar Khayyam," the renowned Persian poem extolling a life of pleasure.

He was born Hector Hugh Munro, and was raised in Scotland by two puritanical maiden aunts. (He later avenged himself by satirizing the dreary ladies in several impolite short stories.) As a young man, he moved to London, where he wrote political commentary. From 1902 to 1908, he worked on the Continent as a foreign correspondent. Between 1908 and 1914, Saki lived in and near London, writing the short stories for which he was acclaimed. He was killed in action during the First World War.

The typical Saki tale is less than ten pages long, and is marked by a witty, literate style, sharp characterization, and a masterful surprise ending. Like "The Mouse," most of his stories are humorous; but Saki is equally famous as the author of some of the most effective horror stories ever written.

The lady is asleep, he thought...

Now is the time to escape from

THE MOUSE

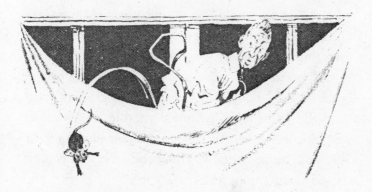

THEODORIC VOLER had been brought up, from infancy to the confines of middle age, by a fond mother whose chief solicitude had been to keep him screened from what she called the coarser realities of life. When she died she left Theodoric alone in a world that was as real as ever, and a good deal coarser than he considered it had any need to be.

To a man of his temperament and upbringing even a simple railway journey was crammed with petty annoyances and minor discords, and as he settled himself down in a second-class compartment one September morning he was conscious of ruffled feelings and general mental distress and discomposure.

He had been staying at a country vicarage, the inmates of which had been certainly neither brutal nor bacchanalian, but their supervision of the domestic establishment had been of that lax order which invites disaster. The pony carriage that was to take him to the station had never been properly ordered, and when the moment for his departure drew near the handyman who should have produced the required article was nowhere to be found. In this emergency Theodoric, to his mute but very intense disgust, found himself obliged to collaborate with the vicar's daughter in the task of harnessing the pony, which necessitated groping about in an ill-lighted outhouse called a stable, and smelling very like one—except in patches where it smelt of mice. Without being actually afraid of mice, Theodoric classed them among the coarser incidents of life, and considered that Providence, with a little exercise of moral courage, might long ago have recognized that they were not indispensable, and have withdrawn them from circulation.

As the train glided out of the station Theodoric's nervous imagination accused himself of exhaling a weak odor of stable-yard, and possibly of displaying a moldy straw or two on his usually well-brushed garments. Fortunately the only other occupant of the compartment, a lady of about the same age as himself, seemed inclined for slumber rather than scrutiny. The train was not due to stop till the terminus was reached, in about an hour's time, and the carriage was of the old-fashioned sort, that held no communication with a corridor; therefore no further traveling companions were likely to intrude on Theodoric's semi-privacy.

And yet the train had scarcely attained its normal speed before he became reluctantly but vividly aware that he was not alone with the slumbering lady; he was not even alone in his own clothes. A warm, creeping movement over his flesh betrayed the unwelcome and highly resented presence, unseen but poignant, of a strayed mouse, that had evidently dashed into its present retreat during the episode of the pony harnessing. Furtive stamps and shakes and wildly directed pinches failed to dislodge the intruder, whose motto, indeed, seemed to be Excelsior; and the lawful occupant of the clothes lay back against the cushions and endeavored rapidly to evolve some means for putting an end to the dual ownership.

It was unthinkable that he should continue for the space of a whole hour in the horrible position of a Rowton House for vagrant mice (already his imagination had at least doubled the numbers of the alien invasion). On the other hand, nothing less drastic than partial disrobing would ease him of his tormentor, and to undress in the presence of a lady, even for so laudable a purpose, was an idea that made his ear-tips tingle in a blush of abject shame. He had never been able to bring himself even to the mild exposure of open-work socks in the presence of the fair sex.

And yet—the lady in this case was to all appearances soundly and securely asleep; the mouse, on the other hand, seemed to be trying to crowd a Wanderjahr into a few strenuous minutes. If there is any truth in the theory of transmigration, this particular mouse must certainly have been in a former state a member of the Alpine Club. Sometimes in its eagerness it lost its footing and slipped for half an inch or so; and then, in fright, or more probably temper, it bit.

Theodoric was goaded into the most audacious undertaking of his life. Crimsoning to the hue of a beetroot and keeping an agonized watch on his slumbering fellow-traveler, he swiftly and noiselessly secured the ends of his railway-rug to the racks on either side of the carriage, so that a substantial curtain hung athwart the compartment. In the narrow dressing-room that he had thus improvised he proceeded with violent haste to extricate himself partially and the mouse entirely from the surrounding casings of tweed and half-wool.

As the unraveled mouse gave a wild leap to the floor, the rug, slipping its fastening at either end, also came down with a heart-curdling flop, and almost simultaneously the awakened sleeper opened her eyes. With a movement almost quicker than the mouse's, Theodoric pounced on the rug, and hauled its ample folds chin-high over his dismantled person as he collapsed into the further corner of the carriage.

The blood raced and beat in the veins of his neck and forehead, while he waited dumbly for the communication cord to be pulled. The lady, however, contented herself with a silent stare at her strangely muffled companion. How much had she seen, Theodoric queried to himself, and in any case what on earth must she think of his present posture?

"I think I have caught a chill," he ventured desperately.

"Really, I'm sorry," she replied. "I was just going to ask you if you would open this window."

"I fancy it's malaria," he added, his teeth chattering slightly, as much from fright as from a desire to support his theory.

"I've got some brandy in my hold-all, if you'll kindly reach it down for me," said his companion.

"Not for worlds—I mean, I never take anything for it," he assured her earnestly.

"I suppose you caught it in the Tropics?"

Theodoric, whose acquaintance with the Tropics was limited to an annual present of a chest of tea from an uncle in Ceylon, felt that even the malaria was slipping from him. Would it be possible, he wondered, to disclose the real state of affairs to her in small installments?

"Are you afraid of mice?" he ventured, growing, if possible, more scarlet in the face.

"Not unless they came in quantities, like those that ate up Bishop Hatto. Why do you ask?"

"I had one crawling inside my clothes just now," said Theodoric in a voice that hardly seemed his own. "It was a most awkward situation."

"It might have been, if you wear your clothes at all tight," she observed; "but mice have strange ideas of comfort."

"I had to get rid of it while you were asleep," he

continued; then, with a gulp, he added, "it was getting rid of it that brought me to—to this."

"Surely leaving off one small mouse wouldn't bring on a chill," she exclaimed, with a levity that Theodoric accounted abominable.

Evidently she had detected something of his predicament, and was enjoying his confusion. All the blood in his body seemed to have mobilized in one concentrated blush, and an agony of abasement, worse than a myriad mice, crept up and down over his soul.

And then, as reflection began to assert itself, sheer terror took the place of humiliation. With every minute that passed the train was rushing nearer to the crowded and bustling terminus where dozens of prying eyes would be exchanged for the one paralyzing pair that watched him from the further corner of the carriage.

There was one slender despairing chance, which the next few minutes must decide. His fellow-traveler might relapse into a blessed slumber. But as the minutes throbbed by, that chance ebbed away. The furtive glance which Theodoric stole at her from time to time disclosed only an unwinking wakefulness.

"I think we must be getting near now," she presently observed.

Theodoric had already noted with growing terror the recurring stacks of small, ugly dwellings that heralded the journey's end. The words acted as a signal. Like a hunted beast breaking cover and dashing madly towards some other haven of momentary safety, he threw aside his rug and struggled frantically into his disheveled garments. He was conscious of dull suburban stations racing past the window, of a choking, hammering sensation in his throat and heart, and of an icy silence in that corner towards which he dared not look.

Then as he sank back in his seat, clothed and almost delirious, the train slowed down to a final crawl, and the woman spoke.

"Would you be so kind," she asked, "as to get me a porter to put me into a cab? It's a shame to trouble you when you're feeling unwell, but being blind makes one so helpless at a railway station."

HANNIBAL COONS (1909-   )

. . . has been a professional humorist since 1939. His older brother, who wrote under the name of Armitage Trail, was a much published detective story writer. Coons lives in California with his wife and a large gray cat. He is an ardent golfer.

The first of the "Dear George" stories was written in 1948. During the next eight years, these sagas of a madcap letter-writing publicity man appeared regularly in "Collier's" magazine.

When early in 1957 "Collier's" folded, Coons switched from magazine to television writing. He has been associated with several major network shows. Since '57, George has written no more letters, but the odds are good for a comeback in Coons' medium.

He set out with an actress

and six cannibals on the

CHICAGO SAFARI

FEDERAL PICTURES
Hollywood, California

From RICHARD L. REED
Director of Publicity

July 6, 1951
Air Mail

Mr. George Seibert
Special Representative, Federal Pictures
Hotel Mayflower
Washington, D.C.

Dear George:

Well, George, you can call a halt to that fool gum-shoe activity there. We've shelved the Alaskan deal, so just rub noses all around, tell everybody we'll see them later, and thanks a lot.

As is not unusual in this business, we are off in another direction. Do you own anything decent in the way of a pith helmet? Anything you'd want to go out in? If not, purchase one immediately; they are becoming an absolute necessity in the movie business. Any studio today that isn't making at least one picture in darkest Africa just isn't in it at all. There's one sport at which we're undisputed world's champions out here, and that's follow-the-leader. King Solomon's Mines makes money, and boom! Africa is so crowded with actors there is hardly any space left for the animals. From now on if a lion isn't in the picture, he can't get a room, and that's that. If you and I had any sense, we'd quit this publicity dodge, open a branch of the Brown Derby at Nairobi, and make a fortune.

At any rate, till this travel epidemic blows over, just think of us as Burton Holmes. If people want a look at some of these foreign lands they're reading about, Heaven knows we're willing to oblige. So willing we'd almost take home movies of people's children if the people would promise to attend.

But at the moment we're all of course busy in Africa. And with a cartload of African epics either already playing or about due to open, who has had the only original idea in the proceedings? Me.

The problem, as usual, has been how to give our own horn the loudest toot. Our thing, Nairobi Nights, is not a bad African travelogue at all, but most of the others, from what we hear, are just as genuine. So how to stand out?

Then I got it. The other day our elegant Mr. Conrad J. Thorne, who directed the epic, was showing us some of the crates of souvenirs and relics he brought back with him to impress his Palm Springs houseguests. And the stuff was really interesting. At least I'd never seen a lot of the things, and I'm not exactly a stay-at-home. And suddenly I thought: If this stuff is interesting to me, it ought to be to others. And in no time we whipped up the plans.

We are going to start the picture off with what we hope will be quite a bang by taking a fast road tour of the big cities, with Director Thorne and several of the stars going along to show the audiences all the actual stuff they brought back and telling some of their interesting and very genuine experiences during the making of the picture. And the kicker will be when Thorne brings out six genuine African cannibals, or head-hunters, or whatever they call those native jokers over there, who will proceed to scare everybody half to death with some tribal dances and very real spear-tossing.

Which is where you come in.

Because at this very moment our six African head-hunters are approaching New York from Nairobi on the SS Spitsbergen. And somebody has to meet them, welcome them to our shores, and see that they get to Chicago by Friday. We've done the main rehearsing here, and Thorne and the others will go direct to Chicago, where the thing opens Sunday.

Beautiful Rebecca Lane, the blonde lady star of the picture, is in New York, but she'll fly directly out by herself, also getting there Friday.

So as you can see, there's really no problem at all, except for somebody to meet these fun-loving head-hunters—six-thirty Monday morning, Pier 6—and get the safari started for Chicago. I'd love to do it myself, as you know, but I'm needed here.

So guess who has drawn this plum of an assignment? Right.

I'm leaving everything to you, including the mode of transportation. There are floods all over that end of the country, so go by canoe if you want to, just so you're in Chicago by Friday. Do whatever you think best after you meet them and size up the situation.

There's nothing to it. You shouldn't have any trouble at all locating them. Unless it's a cruise ship, they'll be the only people getting off the boat naked and carrying spears.

Love,

Dick

RICHARD L. REED
FEDERAL PICTURES HOLLYWOOD
CALIF

THANKS, BUT DON'T NEED ANY HEAD-HUNTERS TO HUNT MINE. I KNOW RIGHT WHERE IT IS. AND RIGHT WHERE I INTEND TO KEEP IT.

GEORGE

GEORGE SEIBERT
HOTEL MAYFLOWER WASH DC

OH, GEORGE, DON'T GET DRAMATIC. THESE GUYS
WORK FOR US. PROBABLY ALL GRADUATES OF OXFORD.
AUTHORITIES ON NATIVE ARTS AND CRAFTS. THE ONLY
POSSIBLE DANGER IS THAT YOU MIGHT HAVE TO BUY
A BASKET.

DICK

RICHARD L. REED
FEDERAL PICTURES HOLLYWOOD
CALIF

THAT'S WHAT I'M AFRAID OF—TO CARRY MY HEAD
IN. LOOK, DICK, I'M ALWAYS HAPPY TO SERVE IN ANY
REASONABLE WAY, BUT WHEN YOU GET INTO THE
CANNIBAL DEPARTMENT I SAY YOU'RE CARRYING GEN-
UINENESS TOO FAR. SUPPOSE I JUST TURN THIS WHOLE
PROJECT OVER TO THE NATIONAL GEOGRAPHIC—THEIR
OFFICE IS NOT OVER TWO BLOCKS FROM THIS HOTEL—
AND THEN GET BACK TO MY WORK. OKAY?

GEORGE

GEORGE SEIBERT
HOTEL MAYFLOWER WASH DC

WHY CAN'T THIS PLACE GET ME ONE DECENT ASSIST-
ANT? GEORGE, THESE GUYS WERE PERSONALLY PICKED
FOR US BY OLD BILL JENKINS AT NAIROBI, WHO HIRED
ALL THE NATIVES WE USED IN THE PICTURE, AND WHO
WOULDN'T DARE LET US DOWN. AND YOU KNOW IT.
AND IF YOU SEND ME ONE MORE SUPPOSEDLY WITTY
TELEGRAM YOU'LL HAVE SOMETHING WORSE THAN
CANNIBALS TO DEAL WITH. MEANING ME. NOW GET
GOING, GEORGE.

RICHARD L. REED

RICHARD L. REED
FEDERAL PICTURES HOLLYWOOD
CALIF

   YES SIR.

                                        GEORGE

                    HOTEL STATLER
                  New York, New York

                                    July 9, 1951
                                    Air Mail Special

Mr. Richard L. Reed
Director of Publicity, Federal Pictures
Hollywood, California

Dear Dick:

Well, if anyone had asked me, I would have said no, Hollywood could no longer surprise me. Mine eyes had seen the glory, twenty years of it, and there was just nothing else to be seen.

Well, let me be the first to say that I was wrong. This time you have really blown the cork.

Dick, I can't take this collection of savages on a road tour any more than I could take an active volcano on a road tour. It's an interesting idea, but it just won't work. You may be kidding, but these guys aren't. They've got very mean expressions. And every time they look at me, the look says, H'mm, long pig. They don't speak a word of any language that anybody ever heard of, and their entire costume consists of four medium-size feathers, located not at all strategically. And their armament consists not only of spears, but huge knives, heavy enough, I would say, to cut the average bungalow in two. And when anybody approaches them, they swing them as though doing dumbbell exercises. Sa-wish!

Somebody, lad, has just sent us the wrong merchandise. When you start dealing with the African Sears, Roebuck, you'll just have to start typing the orders, instead of scribbling them in longhand this way. The captain of the Spitsbergen, an old Norwegian named Sorensen, and a man not noticeably nervous, brought these characters over in the brig. Sorensen said, yes, he knew that we'd paid first-class passage for them, but he yoost felt more comfortable that way. And they evidently didn't mind.

But having crossed, what now? Phineas T. Barnum, even as a young man, would have refused to accept this shipment. They're still in Captain Sorensen's cozy brig, and it's a *status quo* I see no reason to disturb. The Spitsbergen will be here several days loading, and the only thing I see to do is to leave them right there, pay Captain Sorensen their return passage—whatever the brig costs—and have him take them back where they came from.

I say have a care. And let's start now.

As ever,
George

GEORGE SEIBERT
HOTEL STATLER NEW YORK NY

GEORGE, WHY DON'T YOU HIRE A BABY SITTER FOR
A COUPLE OF NIGHTS? TILL YOU GET OVER THIS AT-
TACK OF THE VAPORS. IN OTHER WORDS, LITTLE RED
RIDINGHOOD, LET'S GET THOSE POOR GUYS OUT OF
THAT BRIG AND GET GOING. INCIDENTALLY, WHEN
WE NEED YOUR ADVICE ON POLICY MATTERS, WE'LL
WIRE YOU. DON'T CALL US. WE'LL CALL YOU. AND NOW
LET'S GET THIS SHOW ON THE ROAD. EH?

DICK

HOTEL STATLER
New York, New York

July 10, 1951
Air Mail

Mr. Richard L. Reed,
Director of Publicity, Federal Pictures
Hollywood, California

Dear Dick:

Have you ever been a prize-fight manager? You re-
mind me so much of one. "They can't lick us. Now
get out there and punch that guy." Three thousand
miles from danger, you are one of the bravest men I
have ever known.

But, so be it. I guess any army needs both generals
and corporals.

And realizing that you would no doubt take your usual deep interest in my personal safety, I decided that the only thing to do was to try somehow to get acquainted with these pantless Thespians, and see if there was any chance at all of getting them to Chicago alive. Of getting them to Chicago with me alive, that is.

So, laying in certain supplies, I fastened my safety belt and took off for Pier 6. Squatting down in front of the brig door, I uncovered a large platter of fried chicken legs and said, "Me white man. Me like you. Me got lots fried chicken. You like?"

Well, what they should have done, of course, was to answer in perfect English, with a request for finger bowls. But unfortunately this wasn't vaudeville. What they actually did was to give me a particularly frightening glare, grab the chicken without a word, and gulp it down.

Well.

Next I tried bananas and assorted fruit. Then more chicken. Then more bananas. And when I was definitely sure that they couldn't eat another bite of anything, I said, "Me George. Me George Seibert. Sighbert. Me friend. Me coming in to give you nice presents."

Well, I didn't know that I was known even in Africa, but evidently I am because they at least stopped swinging their blasted cutlasses. And unlocking the brig door—dropping the key only four times in the process—I entered. Passing out gifts. Hurriedly. I had stopped at a costume house on the way over, and secured an armload of old musical-comedy costumes. And they loved them. I don't believe that I have reported that they're all men—there's little doubt of that —which simplified my shopping greatly. "You like?" I said, handing out my treasures with a broad, if somewhat tight, smile.

And suddenly they started grinning back, and the battle was won. In fifteen minutes we were the best of friends, grinning, slapping each other on the back, comparing wrist watches and spears, and having a very dickens of a time. Captain Sorensen was standing outside, looking as though at any moment he might slap the door shut on all of us.

At any rate, you can forget this one. We're off to Chicago.

Relieved regards,
George

GEORGE SEIBERT
HOTEL STATLER NEW YORK NY

GEORGE BOY, GET OUT OF THERE. YOU WERE RIGHT IN THE FIRST PLACE. THOSE CHARACTERS ARE FAR TOO UNCIVILIZED TO ATTEMPT TO TAKE ON A ROAD TOUR. LEAVE THEM RIGHT IN THAT BRIG AND WAIT FOR IMPORTANT AIR-MAIL LETTER.

DICK

From RICHARD L. REED
Director of Publicity

July 10, 1951
Air Mail Special

Mr. George Seibert
Special Representative, Federal Pictures
Hotel Statler
New York, New York

Dear George:

George, how glad I am that I caught you before you started out with those anteaters.

That blowhard Thorne almost got us in a terrific jam. That's the trouble with good directors—they keep getting themselves confused with Superman. When Conrad J. Thorne is directing an aviation picture, he once taught the Wright brothers all they knew. On a cowboy epic he was once the world's greatest bull-dogger; tells everybody in sight just how to board their horses. FBI picture—he singlehanded captured most of the early-day desperadoes. Also, as you know, he started everybody in show business who's ever been in show business, and in general he just blows it all times like a bassoon.

Well, it seems that while they were over there making this African thing, he had a brand-new audience, and accordingly outdid himself. I'm told he wore an old threadbare bush jacket at all times, carried a loaded elephant gun draped across his arm, and around the campfire, nights, he talked for hours about how he had put down native revolts in New Zealand, and killed tigers in India armed only with a willow switch.

And now it appears that his busy larynx has finally backfired. Not on him, as unfair fate would have it, but on us. I've just had a letter from Bill Jenkins at Nairobi asking if the natives he sent us were genuine enough. He said that he knew that any such noted explorer as Mr. Thorne would want only grade-A savages, so he'd gone out of his way to find us some; he'd gone clear up into the back country and got us half a dozen of the most completely uncivilized savages in all Africa. He said when these guys ate an explorer they ate boots and all. He said that actually we shouldn't have any real trouble with them, but that he would advise us to keep Mr. Thorne in direct charge at all times, as otherwise they might have somebody's head on a pole.

Well, that naturally tears it.

Due to gabby Mr. Thorne, the great Poo-Bah of everything, we've spent a lot of time and money bringing over six such completely genuine savages that we don't dare even open the box.

The cannibal business is, of course, silly, as we can certainly keep them supplied with food. And after all, we usually have cops available in this country. But if those six big guys should suddenly get mad at something and start swinging those neck choppers, we could still find ourselves in quite a mess.

It certainly is lucky I caught you.

If you'd started out alone with those characters, things could very easily have got out of hand. In ways that stagger the mind.

We could have got into some damage suits that would have made legal history. In addition to the possible nuisance of burying what was left of you.

Whew! There are times when I think that I'm underpaid.

As ever,
Dick

HOTEL STATLER
New York, New York

July 11, 1951
Air Mail

Mr. Richard L. Reed
Director of Publicity, Federal Pictures
Hollywood, California

Dear Dick:

Just a fast note to say that I haven't got time to wait for your letter, whatever it is. I'll just have to hope that it isn't anything important. Because we have to leave for Chicago this afternoon. The Spitsbergen is loaded and ready to pull out for the return trip to Africa, and I've got to get our laughing boys out of the brig and off by three o'clock.

I've decided to make the trip by car, because I've got a wonderful idea. Now that I know that these guys aren't really dangerous, just that they look fierce, all we have to do is hold out our hand to get about forty million dollars' worth of publicity.

Here's the deal. We are on our way to Chicago to join a stage show in conjunction with the great Federal Pictures epic of darkest Africa, Nairobi Nights—right? We definitely have to be there by Friday, so we wouldn't logically dawdle—right? We are taking them by car because they are so completely uncivilized that we don't dare take them by train or plane—right? And between us and Chicago at this moment, particularly in Ohio, there are at least two dozen rivers of assorted sizes, all overflowing like a child's sand bucket—right?

Well, just before we leave this afternoon I will call the Weather Bureau and find out just where along our route I can expect a really rousing flood. We will then proceed there at full speed, splash as far into same as the car will go, and become thoroughly marooned. We'll be lost for days. While you and the nation's reporters scour the countryside to much huzza and headline. With you pretending great alarm. Everybody will accept the gag as genuine because the big opening at Chicago will actually be delayed, and who would be fool enough to do that?

Then, say late on the second day, I will fight my way through to a rescue station, nearer dead than alive, and just before losing consciousness gasp out the news that in a desperate effort to save our lives we all took off in different directions in search of help, and thus half a dozen genuine African cannibals are loose on the land, oh, heaven help the state of Ohio. I will then faint. So, if I am any judge of people, will most of the citizens of Ohio. Because with that you will have to admit reluctantly the whole chilling story, and the headlines will balloon as though printed on yeast cakes.

Did you ever hear a better idea in your life?

It's foolproof. I'll have a big hamper of fried chicken along, and, properly fed, these boys wouldn't hurt a flea. And it can't be any trouble finding them later and rounding them up. Believe me, they don't look at all like anyone else in Ohio. And there's no danger of drowning them—any native I've ever heard of can swim like a fish.

So what could go wrong? It's the chance of a lifetime. If they make anybody along the way or at a motel nervous, I'll just say they're a bunch of wrestlers I'm driving to Des Moines.

All you have to do is quit worrying and make a tremendous uproar when we don't arrive in Chicago on time. Try to seem genuinely concerned.

And leave the rest to me.

Hasty regards,
George

P.S. Oh, one other thing. I just called Rebecca Lane and talked her into riding along with us instead of taking the plane. On a deal like this a beautiful girl can be useful in so many ways. She can't do anything in Chicago till the rest of us get there anyway, and I've just thought of a wonderful way to work her into the publicity.

When we become marooned, instead of all of us scattering in search of aid, I, brave George, shall go forth alone through the raging waters, leaving Rebecca behind with our trusty head-hunters. Because why? Because in getting out of the flooded car she will have cruelly injured her ankle, making further travel on her part impossible. And the reason I will also have to leave our fun-loving savages behind is because they are very valuable, at least to us, and I don't want any excited citizen sighting one and possibly shooting him deader than a mackerel. Which, as I now realize, could easily happen if they just all took off across country willy-nilly. Far better, if possible, to keep them in a group. Just as upsetting to the populace, and safer for all.

And believe me, Rebecca will be in no danger whatever. All she'll have to do is pass out the sandwiches and bananas at frequent intervals and sort of chaperon everything till I can get back with the constables and photographers.

I haven't told her the full details of the plan as yet; I thought it best to explain it to her as we go along.

At any rate, being forced to leave beautiful blonde Rebecca Lane alone with them, even for a few hours, might be all we'd need to turn this thing into a truly front-page smash. And all so logical. I understand that in the picture she manages thousands of natives on her huge zebra ranch, so how perfectly natural for her to manage six of them while I go for help. Thus saving the countryside.

What a jackpot we have come upon. Just try to act excited and leave everything else to me.

CHIEF, OHIO HIGHWAY PATROL
COLUMBUS O

QUICK. MATTER OF LIFE OR DEATH. AT ANY COST APPREHEND CAR NOW OR SHORTLY TRAVERSING YOUR STATE CONTAINING FILM STAR REBECCA LANE, A DEMENTED PUBLICITY EMPLOYEE OF OURS NAMED GEORGE SEIBERT, AND SIX AFRICAN SAVAGES. USE DUE CAUTION AND WIRE ME IMMEDIATELY UPON APPRE-HENSION. I'LL EXPLAIN LATER. I'D EXPLAIN NOW BUT YOU WOULDN'T BELIEVE IT.

> RICHARD L. REED
> DIRECTOR OF PUBLICITY
> FEDERAL PICTURES
> HOLLYWOOD CALIF

RICHARD L. REED
FEDERAL PICTURES HOLLYWOOD
CALIF

WHAT TYPE CAR ARE SUSPECTS DRIVING?

> H. L. TWINE, SUPERINTENDENT
> OHIO STATE HIGHWAY PATROL

H. L. TWINE, SUPERINTENDENT
OHIO STATE HIGHWAY PATROL
COLUMBUS O

HOW DO I KNOW? JUST FIND IT.

RICHARD L. REED

RICHARD L. REED
FEDERAL PICTURES HOLLYWOOD
CALIF

YOU DON'T KNOW WHAT TYPE OF CAR YOUR OWN
EMPLOYEES ARE DRIVING?

H. L. TWINE

H. L. TWINE, SUPERINTENDENT
OHIO STATE HIGHWAY PATROL
COLUMBUS O

NO, AND NEITHER WOULD YOU IF YOU KNEW
GEORGE. HE COULD BE DRIVING A STUTZ BEARCAT OR
A STANLEY STEAMER CONVERTIBLE. WHAT DOES IT
MATTER WHAT HE'S DRIVING? HOW MANY CARS ARE
THERE ON YOUR ROADS CONTAINING SIX NAKED
SAVAGES?

RICHARD L. REED

RICHARD L. REED
FEDERAL PICTURES HOLLYWOOD
CALIF

IF YOU PERSIST IN JOKING I SIMPLY CAN'T HELP YOU.
WHY DON'T YOU TRY IT AGAIN TOMORROW?

H. L. TWINE

H. L. TWINE, SUPERINTENDENT
OHIO STATE HIGHWAY PATROL
COLUMBUS O

OKAY, DROP DEAD. I'LL CALL THE AP.

RICHARD L. REED

CANNIBALS INVADE OHIO

COLUMBUS, O., July 13 (AP)—Tonight the beleaguered citizens of flood-stricken Ohio were faced
with a new and fantastic danger—an influx of African
cannibals! . . .

RICHARD L. REED
FEDERAL PICTURES HOLLYWOOD
CALIF

ATTABOY, DICK, YOU SOLD IT. AND ON THE FRONT
PAGE! YOU MUST HAVE GIVEN A TRULY STIRRING PER-
FORMANCE. HAS A PUBLICITY MAN EVER WON AN
OSCAR? BY THE WAY, WE'RE OF COURSE DOING FINE.
ALL WELL HERE. I'M KEEPING THESE CHARACTERS SO
FULL OF VITTLES THEY CAN HARDLY BEAR TO LOOK
AT FOOD OF ANY SORT. YOU COULD LEAVE THEM
ALONE IN A DELICATESSEN, AND THEY WOULDN'T
TOUCH A THING. I DO WISH THOUGH THAT THEY'D
STOP SHARPENING THOSE BIG KNIVES FOR A FEW MIN-
UTES. I SHOULD NEVER HAVE BOUGHT THEM THE
WHETSTONES. BUT I THOUGHT IT WOULD KEEP THEM
OCCUPIED, WHICH I MAY SAY IT HAS. ANYWAY, IT
WON'T BE LONG NOW. I EXPECT TO GET US MAROONED
SOMETIME TOMORROW MORNING. BETTER YOU NOT
KNOW EXACTLY WHERE. JUST KEEP UP THE ALARM.
YOU'RE DOING FINE.

GEORGE

H. L. TWINE, SUPERINTENDENT
OHIO STATE HIGHWAY PATROL
COLUMBUS O

QUICK, TWINE, JUST HAD WIRE FROM MISSING PARTY SENT FROM EAST LIVERPOOL, OHIO. THEY'RE JUST ENTERING YOUR STATE ON THE WAY TO CHICAGO. NOW LET'S GET GOING AND FIND THEM. SEND OUT ALL CARS. IN FLOODED AREAS GET ROWBOATS. GET THE QUEEN MARY. ONLY I BEG OF YOU FIND OLD GEORGE. OH, THE HORROR OF IT ALL. TO BE EATEN BY CANNIBALS AT EAST LIVERPOOL, OHIO.

RICHARD L. REED

RICHARD L. REED
FEDERAL PICTURES HOLLYWOOD
CALIF

ALL NIGHT SEARCH CONTINUING INTO THIS MORNING DISCLOSES NO TRACE OF SUSPECTS. THEY CAN'T POSSIBLY BE IN OHIO. HAVE YOU TRIED INDIANA?

H. L. TWINE

H. L. TWINE, SUPERINTENDENT
OHIO STATE HIGHWAY PATROL
COLUMBUS O

NO, AND NEITHER HAVE I TRIED WYOMING. THEY HAVE TO BE THERE SOMEWHERE. LOOK UNDER YOUR DESK.

RICHARD L. REED

SEARCH NARROWS FOR OHIO CANNIBALS

COLUMBUS, O., July 15 (AP)—This afternoon H. L. Twine, Superintendent of the Ohio State Highway Patrol, said that the search for the six missing African head-hunters and film star Rebecca Lane now centers on the area just north of East Liverpool, Ohio, where early this morning hundreds of motorists were marooned when a dam on the upper Ohio River gave way at Sanders Mill. Rescue parties are working desperately to get boats through to the affected area, as the stranded motorists are without food, and no doubt unaware that African cannibals are possibly loose among them. . . .

STUDIO OFFERS $50,000 REWARD TO FINDER OF MISSING FILM PARTY—(AP)

MISSING CANNIBALS FOUND

SANDERS MILL, O., July 15 (AP)—Tonight the attention of an entire nation was centered on this tiny flood-bound Ohio hamlet, where not over an hour ago the grisly search ended for the six missing African head-hunters. The search ended when George Seibert, veteran Federal Pictures publicity man, staggered into a rescue station, nearer dead than alive, and gasped out the fantastic tale of his flood adventures with film star Rebecca Lane and the six cannibals. . . .

HOTEL TAFT
Sanders Mill, Ohio

July 15, 1951
Air Mail Special

Mr. Richard L. Reed
Directory of Publicity, Federal Pictures
Hollywood, California

Dear Dick:

Well, it's been a busy day. But although a little tired, I hasten to get off this report to fill in a few added details on the wondrous news in the public prints. Even on the front page they often miss a few things, for which praise be.

In the first place, don't be too harsh on Mr. Twine. The reason he couldn't find us in Ohio was because we weren't in Ohio. We were for a few minutes yesterday afternoon, when I sent the wire from East Liverpool, but as soon as we had another sandwich and some more bananas all around, we doubled back into Pennsylvania. Casting about on the road map for a good spot to get marooned, I noticed that we had come right past Johnstown, Pennsylvania, where they had quite a flood in 1889, and the car radio said that the Conemaugh River there was again rising. Well, where could there be a more newsy place to enjoy a flood than at Johnstown?

So bending on all sail, we hastened back there. It was raining cats and dogs, so there were very few people out to wonder who we were. Also, I had fortunately hired a station wagon for the trip, not only for the needed seating room, but because nobody ever wonders at anything they see in a station wagon. In addition, I had purchased rain hats and slickers for all, and actually we looked not unlike any other surveying party.

But to business. What a dirty trick that Johnstown played on us. When we finally arrived, I discovered that they've done a lot of sneaky flood-control work around there, and they're out of the flood business completely. So, since it was apparent that with all the stuff in the papers the hounds must be closing in, we had another sandwich and a handful of bananas at a dim drive-in, and headed back toward Ohio at great speed. The laughing boys enjoying everything immensely, but Miss Lane beginning to look a little wan.

But I pushed on. Ever westward.

Just before we hit the Ohio border we stopped and took over most of the rooms at a ratty little motel where the owners looked as though they couldn't read, and while the others slumbered I planned our next move. I knew that we couldn't get very far into Ohio without the enraged Mr. Twine putting the finger on us, so we needed a flood as near the eastern border as possible. Additional calls to various Weather Bureaus, in my role of Arthur Snead, anxious parent, disclosed that the most likely spot was that upper Ohio region around Sanders Mill.

So, sloshing into town in the station wagon, I found

an all-night restaurant, got a tremendous hamper of food, centering on fried chicken and bananas, and shortly after dawn we were off. Still raining.

Crossing into Ohio at the smallest town I could find on the map, Metropolis, we raced north directly for Sanders Mill.

And to tell you the truth, I almost overdid it. Because just as we got in sight of Sanders Mill, the dam blew.

Dick, have you ever been in a flood? A real flood? Let me tell you that before you know it you can be in more water than you've figured on. In a matter of seconds we were looking not for lowlands, but for highlands.

I will never again criticize the Empire State Building; it is the only sensible form of architecture.

By eight o'clock we had churned our way through to a little rise in the road, where maybe fifty other cars were marooned in an otherwise endless sea of muddy, swirling, tumbling water, which was rapidly rising.

In about two minutes more we were on top of the station wagon, all my bright plans forgotten, and Rebecca was pushing up against me saying, "George, I'm scared." She was probably cold. Before we'd left in the morning, since I fondly thought that this would be the day for photographs, I had had her don one of the little tattered-britches costumes she wears in Nairobi Nights, and, while attractive, it undoubtedly wasn't overly warm. The boys, however, didn't give her a second glance. By their views of clothing, she was dressed to the teeth.

And it was at this point, with the endless muddy river swirling rapidly up around us, making further maneuvers of any sort impossible, that I had the first feeling that I had maybe oversold myself on my own brilliance. Because at this moment two things occurred. I suddenly remembered that in our hasty departure I had left the big hamper of food back at the motel. And second, our African friends, evidently tiring of my management, suddenly dived down into the flooded station wagon, retrieved their well-sharpened knives, and came up, ringing the station wagon top like grinning sharks. For a minute I thought we were goners. They couldn't possibly be hungry already, I thought desperately. But then some people just naturally like an early breakfast.

Also at this point, the situation was not helped by the people on the tops of the other cars suddenly sighting them, realizing that they were actually the missing cannibals, and all starting to scream like utter fools.

So what happened? Well, you wouldn't believe it. Never let it be said that everybody in this world doesn't have his purposes.

With all us civilized citizens perched on the tops of our cars, waiting helplessly to be drowned, those six African savages, happy as larks, simply swam over to a group of trees still sticking out of the water, and began building rafts like Henry Kaiser! In no time they had made several dandy rafts, cut pusher poles, and established bus lines to higher ground. Not only for our covey of scared motorists, but for various damp citizens on the surrounding housetops.

And by late afternoon, when one of my beloved head-hunters could pause in his work long enough to pole me over to where I could splash on to the rescue station, I was able to report that due largely to the aid of six African cannibals, not one life was lost at Sanders Mill, Ohio, in the terrible flood of 1951. And tonight, as you certainly know, they are the heroes of the land, and Nairobi Nights is off to a start such as a picture has seldom had. And didn't Rebecca look nice in the newspapers, in her little torn britches, and with her honor guard of cannibals?

Oh, one other thing. A few minutes ago, as I was putting the boys and Rebecca on a chartered plane for Chicago, one of them drew me aside and said, in just dandy English, "Pardon me, Mr. Seibert, but when we get to Chicago how will we know who is Mr. Thorne? We're supposed to give him a little scare for Mr. Jenkins at Nairobi. He talked so much down there that Mr. Jenkins decided somebody ought to give him his comeuppance, as he put it. That's why we acted so foolish when you first came on the boat—we thought you were Mr. Thorne. As soon as you said you were Mr. Seibert, we naturally mended our manners.

"But please don't give us away till we have just a few days to scare Mr. Thorne, because Mr. Jenkins made us promise to do it. And could you do us one more favor, and see that nobody buys us any more bananas for a while? We're all very tired of bananas."

Civilized? They're the glee club from Nairobi Tech!
And now what was that about a $50,000 reward?

As ever,
George

DAMON RUNYON (1884-1946)

. . . broke into print at 13, fought in the Spanish-American War at 14, became a newspaper reporter at 20, and later worked as a sports writer, war correspondent, and syndicated columnist.

In 1932, Runyon published "Guys and Dolls," the first of several short story collections immortalizing New York's gamblers, touts, and other questionable types. His characters are cool and wise-cracking; his situations, hilarious; his idiom, a flowing Broadway slang now called "Runyonese."

A slender, dapper man, a little like the characters he created, Runyon enjoyed hunting and poker, and drank over a gallon of coffee a day. His hangout in New York was Lindy's restaurant; here, thinly disguised as "Mindy's," take place many of his stories, including "A Piece of Pie."

He had to give up

when the lady called for

A PIECE OF PIE

ON BOYLSTON STREET, in the city of Boston, Mass., there is a joint where you can get as nice a broiled lobster as anybody ever slaps a lip over, and who is in there one evening partaking of this tidbit but a character by the name of Horse Thief and me. This Horse Thief is called Horsey for short, and he is not called by this name because he ever steals a horse but because it is the consensus of public opinion from coast to coast that he may steal one if the opportunity presents. Personally, I consider Horsey a very fine character, because any time he is holding anything he is willing to share his good fortune with one and all, and at this time in Boston he is holding plenty. It is the time we make the race meeting at Suffolk Downs, and Horsey gets to going very good, and in fact he is now a character of means, and is my host against the broiled lobster.

Well, at a table next to us are four or five characters who all seem to be well-dressed, and stout-set, and red-faced, and prosperous-looking, and who all speak with the true Boston accent, which consists of many ah's and very few r's. Characters such as these are familiar to anybody who is ever in Boston very much, and they are bound to be politicians, retired cops, or contractors, because Boston is really quite infested with characters of this nature.

I am paying no attention to them, because they are drinking local ale, and talking loud, and long ago I learn that when a Boston character is engaged in aleing himself up, it is a good idea to let him alone, because the best you can get out of him is maybe a boff on the beezer. But Horsey is in there on the old Ear-ie, and very much interested in their conversation, and finally I listen myself just to hear what is attracting his attention, when one of the characters speaks as follows: "Well," he says, "I am willing to bet ten thousand dollars that he can outeat anybody in the United States any time."

Now at this, Horsey gets right up and steps over to the table and bows and smiles in a friendly way on one and all, and says: "Gentlemen," he says, "pardon the intrusion, and excuse me for billing in, but," he says, "do I understand you are speaking of a great eater who resides in your fair city?"

Well, these Boston characters all gaze at Horsey in

such a hostile manner that I am expecting any one of them to get up and request him to let them miss him, but he keeps on bowing and smiling, and they can see that he is a gentleman, and finally one of them says:

"Yes," he says, "we are speaking of a character by the name of Joel Duffle. He is without doubt the greatest eater alive. He just wins a unique wager. He bets a character from Bangor, Me., that he can eat a whole window display of oysters in this very restaurant, and he not only eats all the oysters but he then wishes to wager that he can also eat the shells, but," he says, "it seems that the character from Bangor, Me., unfortunately taps out on the first proposition and has nothing with which to bet on the second."

"Very interesting," Horsey says. "Very interesting, if true, but," he says, "unless my ears deceive me, I hear one of you state that he is willing to wager ten thousand dollars on this eater of yours against anybody in the United States."

"Your ears are perfect," another of the Boston characters says. "I state it, although," he says, "I admit it is a sort of figure of speech. But I state it all right," he says, "and never let it be said that a Conway ever pigs it on a betting proposition."

"Well," Horsey says, "I do not have a tenner on me at the moment, but," he says, "I have here a thousand dollars to put up as a forfeit that I can produce a character who will outeat your party for ten thousand, and as much more as you care to put up."

And with this, Horsey outs with a bundle of coarse

notes and tosses it on the table, and right away one of the Boston characters, whose name turns out to be Carroll, slaps his hand on the money and says: "Bet."

Well, now this is prompt action to be sure, and if there is one thing I admire more than anything else, it is action, and I can see that these are characters of true sporting instincts and I commence wondering where I can raise a few dibs to take a piece of Horsey's proposition, because of course I know that he has nobody in mind to do the eating for his side but Nicely-Nicely Jones. And knowing Nicely-Nicely Jones, I am prepared to wager all the money I can possibly raise that he can outeat anything that walks on two legs. In fact, I will take a chance on Nicely-Nicely against anything on four legs, except maybe an elephant, and at that he may give the elephant a photo finish.

I do not say that Nicely-Nicely is the greatest eater in all history, but what I do say is he belongs up there as a contender. In fact, Professor D., who is a professor in a college out West before he turns to playing the horses for a livelihood, and who makes a study of history in his time, says he will not be surprised but what Nicely-Nicely figures one-two. Professor D. says we must always remember that Nicely-Nicely eats under the handicaps of modern civilization, which require that an eater use a knife and fork, or anyway a knife, while in the old days eating with the hands was a popular custom and much faster. Professor D. says he has no doubt that under the old rules Nicely-Nicely will hang up a record that will endure through the ages, but of course maybe Professor D. overlays Nicely-Nicely somewhat.

Well, now that the match is agreed upon, naturally Horsey and the Boston characters begin discussing where it is to take place, and one of the Boston characters suggests a neutral ground, such as New London, Conn., or Providence, R. I., but Horsey holds out for New York, and it seems that Boston characters are always ready to visit New York, so he does not meet with any great opposition on this point. They all agree on a date four weeks later so as to give the principals plenty of time to get ready, although Horsey and I know that this is really unnecessary as far as Nicely-Nicely is concerned, because one thing about him is he is always in condition to eat.

This Nicely-Nicely Jones is a character who is maybe five feet eight inches tall, and about five feet nine inches wide, and when he is in good shape he will weigh upward of 283 pounds. He is a horse player by trade, and eating is really just a hobby, but he is undoubtedly a wonderful eater even when he is not hungry. Well, as soon as Horsey and I return to New York, we hasten to Mindy's restaurant on Broadway and relate the bet Horsey makes in Boston, and right away so many citizens, including Mindy himself, wish to take a piece of the proposition that it is oversubscribed by a large sum in no time.

Then Mindy remarks that he does not see Nicely-Nicely Jones for a month of Sundays, and then everybody present remembers that they do not see Nicely-

Nicely around lately, either, and this leads to a discussion of where Nicely-Nicely can be, although up to this moment if nobody sees Nicely-Nicely but once in the next ten years it will be considered sufficient. Well, Willie the Worrier, who is a bookmaker by trade, is among those present, and he remembers that the last time he looks for Nicely-Nicely hoping to collect a marker of some years standing, Nicely-Nicely is living at the Rest Hotel in West 49th Street, and nothing will do Horsey but I must go with him over to the Rest to make inquiry for Nicely-Nicely, and there we learn that he leaves a forwarding address away up on Morningside Heights in care of somebody by the name of Slocum.

So Horsey calls a short, and away we go to this address, which turns out to be a five-story walk-up apartment, and a card downstairs shows that Slocum lives on the top floor. It takes Horsey and me ten minutes to walk up the five flights as we are by no means accustomed to exercise of this nature, and when we finally reach a door marked Slocum, we are plumb tuckered out, and have to sit down on the top step and rest awhile. Then I ring the bell at this door marked Slocum, and who appears but a tall young Judy with black hair who is without doubt beautiful, but who is so skinny we have to look twice to see her, and when I ask her if she can give me any information about a party named Nicely-Nicely Jones, she says to me like this: "I guess you mean Quentin," she says. "Yes," she says, "Quentin is here. Come in, gentlemen."

So we step into an apartment, and as we do so a thin, sickly-looking character gets up out of a chair by the window, and in a weak voice says good evening. It is a good evening, at that, so Horsey and I say good evening right back at him, very polite, and then we stand there waiting for Nicely-Nicely to appear, when the beautiful skinny young Judy says: "Well," she says, "this is Mr. Quentin Jones."

Then Horsey and I take another swivel at the thin character, and we can see that it is nobody but Nicely-Nicely, at that, but the way he changes since we last observe him is practically shocking to us both, because he is undoubtedly all shrunk up. In fact, he looks as if he is about half what he is in his prime, and his face is pale and thin, and his eyes are away back in his head, and while we both shake hands with him it is some time before either of us is able to speak. Then Horsey finally says: "Nicely," he says, "can we have a few words with you in private on a very important proposition?"

Well, at this, and before Nicely-Nicely can answer aye, yes or no, the beautiful skinny young Judy goes out of the room and slams a door behind her, and Nicely-Nicely says: "My fiancée, Miss Hilda Slocum," he says. "She is a wonderful character. We are to be married as soon as I lose twenty pounds more. It will take a couple of weeks longer," he says.

"My goodness gracious, Nicely," Horsey says. "What do you mean lose twenty pounds more? You are practically emaciated now. Are you just out of a sick bed, or what?"

"Why," Nicely-Nicely says, "certainly I am not out of a sick bed. I am never healthier in my life. I am on a diet. I lose eighty-three pounds in two months, and am now down to 200. I feel great," he says. "It is all because of my fiancée, Miss Hilda Slocum. She rescues me from gluttony and obesity, or anyway," Nicely-Nicely says, "this is what Miss Hilda Slocum calls it. My, I feel good. I love Miss Hilda Slocum very much," Nicely-Nicely says. "It is a case of love at first sight on both sides the day we meet in the subway. I am wedged in one of the turnstile gates, and she kindly pushes on me from behind until I wiggle through. I can see she has a kind heart, so I date her up for a movie that night and propose to her while the newsreel is on. But," Nicely-Nicely says, "Hilda tells me at once that she will never marry a fat slob. She says I must put myself in her hands and she will reduce me by scientific methods and then she will become my ever-loving wife, but not before. So," Nicely-Nicely says, "I come to live here with Miss Hilda Slocum and her mother, so she can supervise my diet. Her mother is thinner than Hilda. And I surely feel great," Nicely-Nicely says. "Look," he says. And with this, he pulls out the waistband of his pants, and shows enough spare space to hide War Admiral in, but the effort seems to be a strain on him, and he has to sit down in his chair again.

"My goodness gracious," Horsey says. "What do you eat, Nicely?"

"Well," Nicely-Nicely says, "I eat anything that
does not contain starch, but," he says, "of course everything worth eating contains starch, so I really do not
eat much of anything whatever. My fiancée, Miss Hilda
Slocum, arranges my diet. She is an expert dietitian
and runs a widely known department in a diet magazine by the name of *Let's Keep House.*"

Then Horsey tells Nicely-Nicely of how he is
matched to eat against this Joel Duffle, of Boston, for
a nice side bet, and how he has a forfeit of a thousand
dollars already posted for appearance, and how many
of Nicely-Nicely's admirers along Broadway are looking to win themselves out of all their troubles by betting on him, and at first Nicely-Nicely listens with
great interest, and his eyes are shining like six bits, but
then he becomes very sad, and says: "It is no use,
gentlemen," he says. "My fiancée, Miss Hilda Slocum,
will never hear of me going off my diet even for a little
while. Only yesterday I try to talk her into letting me
have a little pumpernickel instead of toasted whole
wheat bread, and she says if I even think of such a thing
again, she will break our engagement. Horsey," he
says, "do you ever eat toasted whole wheat bread for a
month hard running? Toasted?" he says.

"No," Horsey says. "What I eat is nice, white
French bread, and corn muffins, and hot biscuits with
gravy on them."

"Stop," Nicely-Nicely says. "You are eating yourself into an early grave, and, furthermore," he says,
"you are breaking my heart. But," he says, "the more

I think of my following depending on me in this emergency, the sadder it makes me feel to think I am unable to oblige them. However," he says, "let us call Miss Hilda Slocum in on an outside chance and see what her reactions to your proposition are." So we call Miss Hilda Slocum in, and Horsey explains our predicament in putting so much faith in Nicely-Nicely only to find him dieting, and Miss Hilda Slocum's reactions are to order Horsey and me out of the joint with instructions never to darken her door again, and when we are a block away we can still hear her voice speaking very firmly to Nicely-Nicely.

Well, personally, I figure this ends the matter, for I can see that Miss Hilda Slocum is a most determined character, indeed, and the chances are it does end it, at that, if Horsey does not happen to get a wonderful break. He is at Belmont Park one afternoon, and he has a real good thing in a jump race, and when a brisk young character in a hard straw hat and eyeglasses comes along and asks him what he likes, Horsey mentions this good thing, figuring he will move himself in for a few dibs if the good thing connects. Well, it connects all right, and the brisk young character is very grateful to Horsey for his information, and is giving him plenty of much-obliges, and nothing else, and Horsey is about to mention that they do not accept much-obliges at his hotel, when the brisk young character mentions that he is nobody but Mr. McBurgle and that he is the editor of the *Let's Keep House* magazine, and for Horsey to drop in and see him any time he is around his way.

Naturally, Horsey remembers what Nicely-Nicely says about Miss Hilda Slocum working for this *Let's Keep House* magazine, and he relates the story of the eating contest to Mr. McBurgle and asks him if he will kindly use his influence with Miss Hilda Slocum to get her to release Nicely-Nicely from his diet long enough for the contest. Then Horsey gives Mr. McBurgle a tip on another winner, and Mr. McBurgle must use plenty of influence on Miss Hilda Slocum at once, as the next day she calls Horsey up at his hotel before he is out of bed, and speaks to him as follows: "Of course," Miss Hilda Slocum says, "I will never change my attitude about Quentin, but," she says, "I can appreciate that he feels very bad about you gentlemen relying on him and having to disappoint you. He feels that he lets you down, which is by no means true, but it weighs upon his mind. It is interfering with his diet.

"Now," Miss Hilda Slocum says, "I do not approve of your contest, because," she says, "it is placing a premium on gluttony, but I have a friend by the name of Miss Violette Shumberger who may answer your purpose. She is my dearest friend from childhood, but it is only because I love her dearly that this friendship endures. She is extremely fond of eating," Miss Hilda Slocum says. "In spite of my pleadings, and my warnings, and my own example, she persists in food. It is disgusting to me but I finally learn that it is no use arguing with her. She remains my dearest friend," Miss Hilda Slocum says, "though she continues her practice of eating, and I am informed that she is phenomenal in this respect. In fact," she says, "Nicely-Nicely tells me to say to you that if Miss Violette Shumberger can perform the eating exploits I relate to him from hearsay she is a lily. Good-by," Miss Hilda Slocum says. "You cannot have Nicely-Nicely."

Well, nobody cares much about this idea of a stand-in for Nicely-Nicely in such a situation, and especially a Judy that no one ever hears of before, and many citizens are in favor of pulling out of the contest altogether. But Horsey has his thousand-dollar forfeit to think of, and as no one can suggest anyone else, he finally arranges a personal meet with the Judy suggested by Miss Hilda Slocum. He comes into Mindy's one evening with a female character who is so fat it is necessary to push three tables together to give her room for her lap, and it seems that this character is Miss Violette Shumberger. She weighs maybe 250 pounds, but she is by no means an old Judy, and by no means bad-looking. She has a face the size of a town clock and enough chins for a fire escape, but she has a nice smile, and pretty teeth, and a laugh that is so hearty it knocks the whipped cream off an order of strawberry shortcake on a table fifty feet away and arouses the indignation of a customer by the name of Goldstein who is about to consume same. Well, Horsey's idea in bringing her into Mindy's is to get some kind of line on her eating form, and she is clocked by many experts when she starts putting on the hot meat, and it is agreed by one and all that she is by no means a selling-plater. In fact, by the time she gets through, even Mindy admits she has plenty of class, and the upshot of it all is Miss Violette Shumberger is chosen to eat against Joel Duffle.

Maybe you hear something of this great eating contest that comes off in New York one night in the early summer of 1937. Of course eating contests are by no means anything new, and in fact they are quite an old-fashioned pastime in some sections of this country, such as the South and East, but this is the first big public contest of the kind in years, and it creates no little comment along Broadway. In fact, there is some mention of it in the blats, and it is not a frivolous proposition in any respect, and more dough is wagered on it than any other eating contest in history, with Joel Duffle a 6 to 5 favorite over Miss Violette Shumberger all the way through.

This Joel Duffle comes to New York several days before the contest with the character by the name of Conway, and requests a meet with Miss Violette Shumberger to agree on the final details and who shows up with Miss Violette Shumberger as her coach and adviser but Nicely-Nicely Jones. He is even thinner and more peaked-looking than when Horsey and I see him last, but he says he feels great, and that he is within six pounds of his marriage to Miss Hilda Slocum. Well, it seems that his presence is really due to Miss Hilda Slocum herself, because she says that after getting her dearest friend Miss Violette Shumberger into this jack pot, it is only fair to do all she can to help

her win it, and the only way she can think of is to
let Nicely-Nicely give Violette the benefit of his experience and advice, of which he has a great deal.

But afterward we learn that what really happens is
that this editor, Mr. McBurgle, gets greatly interested
in the contest, and when he discovers that in spite of
his influence, Miss Hilda Slocum declines to permit
Nicely-Nicely to personally compete, but puts in a
pinch eater, he is quite indignant and insists on her
letting Nicely-Nicely school Violette. Furthermore
we afterward learn that when Nicely-Nicely returns
to the apartment on Morningside Heights after giving
Violette a lesson, Miss Hilda Slocum always smells
his breath to see if he indulges in any food during his
absence.

Well, this Joel Duffle is a tall character with
stooped shoulders, and a sad expression, and he does
not look as if he can eat his way out of a tea shoppe,
but as soon as he commences to discuss the details of
the contest, anybody can see that he knows what time
it is in situations such as this. In fact, Nicely-Nicely
says he can tell at once from the way Joel Duffle talks
that he is a dangerous opponent, and he says while
Miss Violette Shumberger impresses him as an im-
proving eater, he is only sorry she does not have more
seasoning. This Joel Duffle suggests that the contest
consist of twelve courses of strictly American food,
each side to be allowed to pick six dishes, doing the
picking in rotation, and specifying the weight and
quantity of the course selected to any amount the con-

testant making the pick desires, and each course is
to be divided for eating exactly in half, and after Miss
Violette Shumberger and Nicely-Nicely whisper together for a while, they say the terms are quite satisfactory.

Then Horsey tosses a coin for the first pick, and Joel
Duffle says heads, and it is heads, and he chooses, as
the first course, two quarts of ripe olives, twelve
bunches of celery, and four pounds of shelled nuts,
all this to be split fifty-fifty between them. Miss Violette Shumberger names twelve dozen cherrystone
clams as the second course, and Joel Duffle says two
gallons of Philadelphia pepperpot soup as the third.
Well, Miss Violette Shumberger and Nicely-Nicely
whisper together again, and Violette puts in two five-
pound striped bass, the heads and tails not to count
in the eating, and Joel Duffle names a twenty-two-
pound roast turkey. Each vegetable is rated as one
course, and Miss Violette Shumberger asks for twelve
pounds of mashed potatoes with brown gravy. Joel
Duffle says two dozen ears of corn on the cob, and
Violette replies with two quarts of lima beans. Joel
Duffle calls for twelve bunches of asparagus cooked
in butter, and Violette mentions ten pounds of stewed
new peas. This gets them down to the salad, and it is
Joel Duffle's play, so he says six pounds of mixed green
salad with vinegar and oil dressing, and now Miss
Violette Shumberger has the final selection, which is
the dessert. She says it is a pumpkin pie, two feet
across, and not less than three inches deep.

It is agreed that they must eat with knife, fork or spoon, but speed is not to count, and there is to be no time limit, except they cannot pause more than two consecutive minutes at any stage, except in case of hiccoughs. They can drink anything, and as much as they please, but liquids are not to count in the scoring. The decision is to be strictly on the amount of food consumed, and the judges are to take account of anything left on the plates after a course, but not of loose chewings on bosom or vest up to an ounce. The losing side is to pay for the food, and in case of a tie they are to eat it off immediately on ham and eggs only.

Well, the scene of this contest is the second-floor dining room of Mindy's restaurant which is closed to the general public for the occasion, and only parties immediately concerned in the contest are admitted. The contestants are seated on either side of a big table in the center of the room, and each contestant has three waiters. No talking, and no rooting from the spectators is permitted, but of course in any eating contest the principals may speak to each other if they wish, though smart eaters never wish to do this, as talking only wastes energy, and about all they ever say to each other is please pass the mustard.

About fifty characters from Boston are present to witness the contest, and the same number of citizens of New York are admitted, and among them is this editor, Mr. McBurgle, and he is around asking Horsey if he thinks Miss Violette Shumberger is as good a thing as the jumper at the race track.

Nicely-Nicely arrives on the scene quite early, and his appearance is really most distressing to his old friends and admirers, as by this time he is shy so much weight that he is a pitiful scene, to be sure, but he tells Horsey and me that he thinks Miss Violette Shumberger has a good chance.

"Of course," he says, "she is green. She does not know how to pace herself in competition. But," he says, "she has a wonderful style. I love to watch her eat. She likes the same things I do in the days when I am eating. She is a wonderful character, too. Do you ever notice her smile?" Nicely-Nicely says. "But," he says, "she is the dearest friend of my fiancée, Miss Hilda Slocum, so let us not speak of this. I try to get Hilda to come to see the contest, but she says it is repulsive. Well, anyway," Nicely-Nicely says, "I manage to borrow a few dibs, and am wagering on Miss Violette Shumberger. By the way," he says, "if you happen to think of it, notice her smile."

Well, Nicely-Nicely takes a chair about ten feet behind Miss Violette Shumberger, which is as close as the judges will allow him, and he is warned by them that no coaching from the corners will be permitted, but of course Nicely-Nicely knows this rule as well as they do, and furthermore by this time his exertions seem to have left him without any more energy. There are three judges, and they are all from neutral territory. One of these judges is a party from Baltimore, Md., by the name of Packard, who runs a restaurant, and another is a party from Providence, R. I., by the name

of Croppers, who is a sausage manufacturer. The third
judge is an old Judy by the name of Mrs. Rhubarb,
who comes from Philadelphia, and once keeps an actors' boarding-house, and is considered an excellent
judge of eaters.

Well, Mindy is the official starter, and at 8:30 P.M.
sharp, when there is still much betting among the
spectators, he outs with his watch, and says like this:
"Are you ready, Boston? Are you ready, New York?"
Miss Violette Shumberger and Joel Duffle both nod
their heads, and Mindy says commence, and the contest is on, with Joel Duffle getting the jump at once
on the celery and olives and nuts.

It is apparent that this Joel Duffle is one of these
rough-and-tumble eaters that you can hear quite a distance off, especially on clams and soups. He is also
an eyebrow eater, an eater whose eyebrows go up as
high as the part in his hair as he eats, and this type
of eater is undoubtedly very efficient. In fact, the way
Joel Duffle goes through the groceries down to the
turkey causes the Broadway spectators some uneasi-
ness, and they are whispering to each other that they
only wish the old Nicely-Nicely is in there. But personally, I like the way Miss Violette Shumberger eats
without undue excitement, and with great zest. She
cannot keep close to Joel Duffle in the matter of speed
in the early stages of the contest, as she seems to enjoy
chewing her food, but I observe that as it goes along
she pulls up on him, and I figure this is not because
she is stepping up her pace, but because he is slowing

down.

When the turkey finally comes on, and is split in
two halves right down the middle, Miss Violette
Shumberger looks greatly disappointed, and she
speaks for the first time as follows: "Why," she says
"where is the stuffing?" Well, it seems that nobody
mentions any stuffing for the turkey to the chef, so he
does not make any stuffing, and Miss Violette Shumberger's disappointment is so plain to be seen that the
confidence of the Boston characters is somewhat
shaken. They can see that a Judy who can pack away
as much fodder as Miss Violette Shumberger has to
date, and then beef for stuffing, is really quite an eater.

In fact, Joel Duffle looks quite startled when he
observes Miss Violette Shumberger's disappointment,
and he gazes at her with great respect as she disposes
of her share of the turkey, and the mashed potatoes,
and one thing and another in such a manner that she
moves up on the pumpkin pie on dead even terms with
him. In fact, there is little to choose between them
at this point, although the judge from Baltimore is
calling the attention of the other judges to a turkey leg
that he claims Miss Violette Shumberger does not
clean as neatly as Joel Duffle does his, but the other
judges dismiss this as a technicality.

Then the waiters bring on the pumpkin pie, and
it is without doubt quite a large pie, and in fact it is
about the size of a manhole cover, and I can see that
Joel Duffle is observing this pie with a strange expression on his face, although to tell the truth I do not care

for the expression on Miss Violette Shumberger's face,
either. Well, the pie is cut in two dead center, and one
half is placed before Miss Violette Shumberger, and
the other half before Joel Duffle, and he does not take
more than two bites before I see him loosen his waistband and take a big swig of water, and thinks I to
myself, he is now down to a slow walk, and the pie
will decide the whole heat, and I am only wishing I
am able to wager a little more dough on Miss Violette
Shumberger. But about this moment, and before she
as much as touches her pie, all of a sudden Violette
turns her head and motions to Nicely-Nicely to approach her, and as he approaches, she whispers in his
ear.

Now at this, the Boston character by the name of
Conway jumps up and claims a foul, and several other
Boston characters join him in this claim, and so does
Joel Duffle, although afterwards even the Boston characters admit that Joel Duffle is no gentleman to make
such a claim against a lady. Well, there is some confusion over this, and the judges hold a conference,
and they rule that there is certainly no foul in the actual eating that they can see, because Miss Violette
Shumberger does not touch her pie so far. But they
say that whether it is a foul otherwise all depends on
whether Miss Violette Shumberger is requesting advice
on the contest from Nicely-Nicely and the judge from
Providence, R. I., wishes to know if Nicely-Nicely will
kindly relate what passes between him and Violette
so they may make a decision.

"Why," Nicely-Nicely says, "all she asks me is can I get her another piece of pie when she finishes the one in front of her."

Now at this, Joel Duffle throws down his knife, and pushes back his plate with all but two bites of his pie left on it, and says to the Boston characters like this: "Gentlemen," he says, "I am licked. I cannot eat another mouthful. You must admit I put up a game battle, but," he says, "it is useless for me to go on against this Judy who is asking for more pie before she even starts on what is before her. I am almost dying as it is, and I do not wish to destroy myself in a hopeless effort. Gentlemen," he says, "she is not human."

Well, of course this amounts to throwing in the old napkin and Nicely-Nicely stands up on his chair, and says: "Three cheers for Miss Violette Shumberger!" Then Nicely-Nicely gives the first cheer in person, but the effort overtaxes his strength, and he falls off the chair in a faint just as Joel Duffle collapses under the table, and the doctors at the Clinic Hospital are greatly baffled to receive, from the same address at the same time, one patient suffering from undernourishment, and another who is unconscious from overeating.

Well, in the meantime, after the excitement subsides, and the wagers are settled, we take Miss Violette Shumberger to the main floor in Mindy's for a midnight snack, and when she speaks of her wonderful triumph, she is disposed to give much credit to Nicely-Nicely Jones. "You see," Violette says, "what I really whisper to him is that I am a goner. I whisper to him that I cannot possibly take one bite of the pie if my life depends on it, and if he has any bets down to try and hedge them off as quickly as possible. I fear," she says, "that Nicely-Nicely will be greatly disappointed in my showing, but I have a confession to make to him when he gets out of the hospital. I forget about the contest," Violette says, "and eat my regular dinner of pig's knuckles and sauerkraut an hour before the contest starts, and," she says, "I have no doubt this tends to affect my form somewhat. So," she says, "I owe everything to Nicely-Nicely's quick thinking."

It is several weeks after the great eating contest that I run into Miss Hilda Slocum on Broadway, and it seems to me that she looks much better nourished than the last time I see her, and when I mention this she says: "Yes," she says, "I cease dieting. I learn my lesson," she says. "I learn that male characters do not appreciate anybody who tries to ward off surplus tissue. What male characters wish is substance. Why," she says, "only a week ago my editor, Mr. McBurgle, tells me he will love to take me dancing if only I get something on me for him to take hold of. I am very fond of dancing," she says.

"But," I say, "what of Nicely-Nicely Jones? I do not see him around lately."

"Why," Miss Hilda Slocum says, "do you not hear what this cad does? Why, as soon as he is strong enough to leave the hospital, he elopes with my dearest friend, Miss Violette Shumberger, leaving me a note saying something about two souls with but a sin-

gle thought. They are down in Florida running a bar-
becue stand, and," she says, "the chances are, eating
like seven mules."

When Miss Clarice Van Cleve yelled

HOLD 'EM YALE

BY DAMON RUNYON   *Sam the Gonoph melted*

WHAT I AM DOING in New Haven on the day of a very
large football game between the Harvards and the
Yales is something which calls for quite a little explanation, because I am not such a guy as you will expect to find in New Haven at any time, and especially
on the day of a large football game.

But there I am, and the reason I am there goes back
to a Friday night when I am sitting in Mindy's restaurant on Broadway thinking of very little except how
I can get hold of a few potatoes to take care of the old
overhead. And while I am sitting there, who comes in
but Sam the Gonoph, who is a ticket speculator by
trade, and who seems to be looking all around and
about.

Well, Sam the Gonoph gets to talking to me, and it turns out that he is looking for a guy by the name of Gigolo Georgie, who is called Gigolo Georgie because he is always hanging around night clubs wearing a little mustache and white spats, and dancing with old dolls. In fact, Gigolo Georgie is nothing but a gentleman bum, and I am surprised that Sam the Gonoph is looking for him.

But it seems that the reason Sam the Gonoph wishes to find Gigolo Georgie is to give him a good punch in the snoot, because it seems that Gigolo Georgie promotes Sam for several duckets to the large football game between the Harvards and the Yales to sell on commission, and never kicks back anything whatever to Sam. Naturally Sam considers Gigolo Georgie nothing but a rascal for doing such a thing to him, and Sam says he will find Gogolo Georgie and give him a going-over if it is the last act of his life.

Well, then, Sam explains to me that he has quite a few nice duckets for the large football game between the Harvards and the Yales and that he is taking a crew of guys with him to New Haven the next day to hustle these duckets, and what about me going along and helping to hustle these duckets and making a few bobs for myself, which is an invitation that sounds very pleasant to me, indeed.

Now of course it is very difficult for anybody to get nice duckets to a large football game between the Harvards and the Yales unless they are personally college guys, and Sam the Gonoph is by no means a college guy. In fact, the nearest Sam ever comes to a college is once when he is passing through the yard belonging to the Princetons, but Sam is on the fly at the time as a gendarme is after him, so he does not really see much of the college.

But every college guy is entitled to duckets to a large football game with which his college is connected, and it is really surprising how many college guys do not care to see large football games even after they get their duckets, especially if a ticket spec such as Sam the Gonoph comes along offering them a few bobs more than the duckets are worth. I suppose this is because a college guy figures he can see a large football game when he is old, while many things are taking place around and about that it is necessary for him to see while he is young enough to really enjoy them, such as the Follies.

Anyway, many college guys are always willing to listen when Sam the Gonoph comes around offering to buy their duckets, and then Sam takes these duckets and sells them to customers for maybe ten times the price the duckets call for, and in this way Sam does very good for himself.

I know Sam the Gonoph for maybe twenty years, and always he is speculating in duckets of one kind and another. Sometimes it is duckets for the world's series, and sometimes for big fights, and sometimes it is duckets for nothing but lawn-tennis games, although why anybody wishes to see such a thing as lawn tennis is always a very great mystery to Sam the Gonoph and everybody else.

But in all those years I see Sam dodging around under the feet of the crowds of these large events, or running through the special trains offering to buy or sell duckets, I never hear of Sam personally attending any of these events except maybe a baseball game, or a fight, for Sam has practically no interest in anything but a little profit on his duckets.

He is a short, chunky, black-looking guy with a big beezer, and he is always sweating even on a cold day, and he comes from down around Essex Street, on the lower East Side. Moreover, Sam the Gonoph's crew generally comes from the lower East Side, too, for as Sam goes along he makes plenty of potatoes for himself and branches out quite some, and has a lot of assistants hustling duckets around these different events.

When Sam is younger the cops consider him hard to get along with, and in fact his monicker, the Gonoph, comes from his young days down on the lower East Side, and I hear it is Yiddish for thief, but of course as Sam gets older and starts gathering plenty of potatoes, he will not think of stealing anything. At least not much, and especially if it is anything that is nailed down.

Well, anyway, I meet Sam the Gonoph and his crew at the information desk in Grand Central the next morning, and this is how I come to be in New Haven on the day of the large football game between the Harvards and the Yales.

For such a game as this, Sam has all his best hustlers, including such as Jew Louie, Nubbsy Taylor, Benny

South Street and old Liverlips, and to look at these parties you will never suspect that they are topnotch ducket
hustlers. The best you will figure them is a lot of guys
who are not to be met up with in a dark alley, but then
ducket-hustling is a rough-and-tumble dodge and it
will scarcely be good policy to hire female impersona-
tors.

Now while we are hustling these duckets out around
the main gates of the Yale Bowl I notice a very beautiful little doll of maybe sixteen or seventeen standing
around watching the crowd, and I can see she is waiting for somebody, as many dolls often do at football
games. But I can also see that this little doll is very
much worried as the crowd keeps going in, and it is
getting on toward game time. In fact, by and by I can
see this little doll has tears in her eyes and if there is
anything I hate to see it is tears in a doll's eyes.

So finally I go over to her, and I say as follows:
"What is eating you, little miss?"

"Oh," she says, "I am waiting for Elliot. He is to
come up from New York and meet me here to take
me to the game, but he is not here yet, and I am afraid
something happens to him. Furthermore," she says, the
tears in her eyes getting very large, indeed, "I am afraid
I will miss the game because he has my ticket."

"Why," I say, "this is a very simple proposition. I
will sell you a choice ducket for only a sawbuck, which
is ten dollars in your language, and you are getting such
a bargain only because the game is about to begin, and
the market is going down."

"But," she says, "I do not have ten dollars. In fact, I have only fifty cents left in my purse, and this is worrying me very much, for what will I do if Elliot does not meet me? You see," she says, "I come from Miss Peevy's school at Worcester, and I only have enough money to pay my railroad fare here, and of course I cannot ask Miss Peevy for any money as I do not wish her to know I am going away."

Well, naturally all this is commencing to sound to me like a hard-luck story such as any doll is apt to tell, so I go on about my business because I figure she will next be trying to put the lug on me for a ducket, or maybe for her railroad fare back to Worcester, although generally dolls with hard-luck stories live in San Francisco.

She keeps on standing there, and I notice she is now crying more than somewhat, and I get to thinking to myself that she is about as cute a little doll as ever I see, although too young for anybody to be bothering much about. Furthermore, I get to thinking that maybe she is on the level, at that, with her story.

Well, by this time the crowd is nearly all in the Bowl, and only a few parties such as coppers and hustlers of one kind and another are left standing outside, and there is much cheering going on inside, when Sam the Gonoph comes up looking very much disgusted, and speaks as follows:

"What do you think?" Sam says. "I am left with seven duckets on my hands, and these guys around here will not pay as much as face value for them, and they stand me better than three bucks over that. Well," Sam says, "I am certainly not going to let them go for less than they call for if I have to eat them. What do you guys say we use these duckets ourselves and go in and see the game? Personally," Sam says, "I often wish to see one of these large football games just to find out what makes suckers willing to pay so much for duckets."

Well, this seems to strike one and all, including myself, as a great idea, because none of the rest of us ever see a large football game either, so we start for the gate, and as we pass the little doll who is still crying, I say to Sam the Gonoph like this:

"Listen, Sam," I say, "you have seven duckets, and we are only six, and here is a little doll who is stood up by her guy, and has no ducket, and no potatoes to buy one with, so what about taking her with us?"

Well, this is all right with Sam the Gonoph, and none of the others object, so I step up to the little doll and invite her to go with us, and right away she stops crying and begins smiling, and saying we are very kind indeed. She gives Sam the Gonoph an extra big smile, and right away Sam is saying she is very cute, indeed, and then she gives old Liverlips an even bigger smile, and what is more she takes old Liverlips by the arm and walks with him, and old Liverlips is not only very much astonished, but very much pleased. In fact, old Liverlips begins stepping out very spry, and Liverlips is not such a guy as cares to have any part of dolls, young or old.

But while walking with old Liverlips, the little doll talks very friendly to Jew Louie and to Nubbsy Taylor and Benny South Street, and even to me, and by and by you will think to see us that we are all her uncles, although of course if this little doll really knows who she is with, the chances are she will start chucking faints one after the other.

Anybody can see that she has very little experience in this wicked old world, and in fact is somewhat rattle-headed, because she gabs away very freely about her personal business. In fact, before we are in the Bowl she lets it out that she runs away from Miss Peevy's school to elope with this Elliot, and she says the idea is they are to be married in Hartford after the game. In fact, she says Elliot wishes to go to Hartford and be married before the game.

"But," she says, "my brother John is playing substitute with the Yales today, and I cannot think of getting married to anybody before I see him play, although I am much in love with Elliot. He is a wonderful dancer," she says, "and very romantic. I meet him in Atlantic City last summer. Now we are eloping," she says, "because my father does not care for Elliot whatever. In fact, my father hates Elliot, although he only sees him once, and it is because he hates Elliot so that my father sends me to Miss Peevy's school in Worcester. She is an old pill. Do you not think my father is unreasonable?" she says.

Well, of course none of us have any ideas on such propositions as this, although old Liverlips tells the

little doll he is with her right or wrong, and pretty soon
we are inside the Bowl and sitting in seats as good as
any in the joint. It seems we are on the Harvards' side
of the field, although of course I will never know this
if the little doll does not mention it.

She seems to know everything about this football
business, and as soon as we sit down she tries to point
out her brother playing substitute for the Yales, saying
he is the fifth guy from the end among a bunch of guys
sitting on a bench on the other side of the field all
wrapped in blankets. But we cannot make much of him
from where we sit, and anyway it does not look to me
as if he has much of a job.

It seems we are right in the middle of all the Harvards and they are making an awful racket, what with
yelling, and singing, and one thing and another, because it seems the game is going on when we get in,
and that the Harvards are shoving the Yales around
more than somewhat. So our little doll lets everybody
know she is in favor of the Yales by yelling, "Hold 'em,
Yale!"

Personally, I cannot tell which are the Harvards and
which are the Yales at first, and Sam the Gonoph and
the others are as dumb as I am, but she explains the
Harvards are wearing the red shirts and the Yales the
blue shirts, and by and by we are yelling for the Yales
to hold 'em, too, although of course it is only on account of our little doll wishing the Yales to hold 'em,
and not because any of us care one way or the other.

Well, it seems that the idea of a lot of guys and a

little doll getting right among them and yelling for the Yales to hold 'em is very repulsive to the Harvards around us, although any of them must admit it is very good advice to the Yales, at that, and some of them start making cracks of one kind and another, especially at our little doll. The chances are they are very jealous because she is outyelling them, because I will say one thing for our little doll, she can yell about as loud as anybody I ever hear, male or female.

A couple of Harvards sitting in front of old Liverlips are imitating our little doll's voice, and making guys around them laugh very heartily, but all of a sudden these parties leave their seats and go away in great haste, their faces very pale, indeed, and I figure maybe they are both taken sick the same moment, but afterwards I learn that Liverlips takes a big shiv out of his pocket and opens it and tells them very confidentially that he is going to carve their ears off.

Naturally, I do not blame the Harvards for going away in great haste, for Liverlips is such a looking guy as you will figure to take great delight in carving off ears. Furthermore, Nubbsy Taylor and Benny South Street and Jew Louie and even Sam the Gonoph commence exchanging such glances with other Harvards around us who are making cracks at our little doll that presently there is almost a dead silence in our neighborhood, except for our little doll yelling, "Hold 'em, Yale!" You see by this time we are all very fond of our little doll because she is so cute-looking and has so much zing in her, and we do not wish anybody making cracks at her or at us either, and especially at us.

In fact, we are so fond of her that when she happens to mention that she is a little chilly, Jew Louie and Nubbsy Taylor slip around among the Harvards and come back with four steamer rugs, six mufflers, two pairs of gloves, and a thermos bottle full of hot coffee for her, and Jew Louie says if she wishes a mink coat to just say the word. But she already has a mink coat. Furthermore, Jew Louie brings her a big bunch of red flowers that he finds on a doll with one of the Harvards, and he is much disappointed when she says it is the wrong color for her.

Well, finally the game is over, and I do not remember much about it, although afterwards I hear that our little doll's brother John plays substitute for the Yales very good. But it seems that the Harvards win, and our little doll is very sad indeed about this, and is sitting there looking out over the field, which is now covered with guys dancing around as if they all suddenly go daffy, and it seems they are all Harvards, because there is really no reason for the Yales to do any dancing.

All of a sudden our little doll looks toward one end of the field, and says as follows: "Oh, they are going to take our goal posts!"

Sure enough, a lot of the Harvards are gathering around the posts at this end of the field, and are pulling and hauling at the posts, which seem to be very stout posts, indeed. Personally, I will not give you eight cents for these posts, but afterwards one of the Yales tells me that when a football team wins a game it is considered the proper caper for this team's boosters to grab the other guy's goal posts. But he is not able to tell me what good the posts are after they get them, and this is one thing that will always be a mystery to me.

Anyway, while we are watching the goings-on around the goal posts, our little doll says come on and jumps up and runs down an aisle and out on to the field, and into the crowd around the goal posts, so naturally we follow her. Somehow she manages to wiggle through the crowd of Harvards around the posts, and the next thing anybody knows she shins up one of the posts faster than you can say scat, and pretty soon is roosting out on the cross-bar between the posts like a chipmunk.

Afterwards she explains that her idea is the Harvards will not be ungentlemanly enough to pull down the goal posts with a lady roosting on them, but it seems these Harvards are no gentlemen, and keep on pulling, and the posts commence to teeter, and our little doll is teetering with them, although of course she is in no danger if she falls because she is sure to fall on the Harvards' noggins, and the way I look at it, the noggin of anybody who will be found giving any time to pulling down goal posts is apt to be soft enough to break a very long fall.

Now Sam the Gonoph and old Liverlips and Nubbsy Taylor and Benny South Street and Jew Louie and I reach the crowd around the goal posts at about the same time, and our little doll sees us from her roost and yells to us as follows: "Do not let them take our posts!"

Well, about this time one of the Harvards who seems to be about nine feet high reaches over six other guys and hits me on the chin and knocks me so far that when I pick myself up I am pretty well out of the way of everybody and have a chance to see what is going on.

Afterwards somebody tells me that the guy probably thinks I am one of the Yales coming to the rescue of the goal posts, but I wish to say I will always have a very low opinion of college guys, because I remember two other guys punch me as I am going through the air, unable to defend myself.

Now Sam the Gonoph and Nubbsy Taylor and Jew Louie and Benny South Street and old Liverlips somehow manage to ease their way through the crowd until they are under the goal posts, and our little doll is much pleased to see them, because the Harvards are now making the posts teeter more than somewhat with their pulling, and it looks as if the posts will go any minute.

Of course Sam the Gonoph does not wish any trouble with these parties, and he tries to speak nicely to the guys who are pulling at the posts, saying as follows:

"Listen," Sam says, "the little doll up there does not wish you to take these posts."

Well, maybe they do not hear Sam's words in the confusion, or if they do hear them they do not wish to pay any attention to them, for one of the Harvards mashes Sam's derby hat down over his eyes, and another smacks old Liverlips on the left ear, while Jew Louie and Nubbsy Taylor and Benny South Street are shoved around quite some.

"All right," Sam the Gonoph says, as soon as he can pull his hat off his eyes, "all right, gentlemen, if you wish to play this way. Now, boys, let them have it!"

So Sam the Gonoph and Nubbsy Taylor and Jew Louie and Benny South Street and old Liverlips begin letting them have it, and what they let them have it with is not only their dukes, but with the good old difference in their dukes, because these guys are by no means suckers when it comes to a battle, and they all carry something in their pockets to put in their dukes in case of a fight, such as a dollar's worth of nickels rolled up tight.

Furthermore, they are using the old leather, kicking guys in the stomach when they are not able to hit them on the chin, and Liverlips is also using his noodle to good advantage, grabbing guys by their coat lapels and yanking them into him so he can butt them between the eyes with his noggin, and I wish to say that old Liverlips' noggin is a very dangerous weapon at all times.

Well, the ground around them is soon covered with Harvards, and it seems that some Yales are also mixed up with them, being Yales who think Sam the Gonoph and his guys are other Yales defending the goal posts, and wishing to help out. But of course Sam the Gonoph and his guys cannot tell the Yales from the Harvards, and do not have time to ask which is which, so they are just letting everybody have it who comes along. And while all this is going on our little doll is sitting up on the cross-bar and yelling plenty of encouragement to

Sam and his guys.

Now it turns out that these Harvards are by no means soft touches in a scrabble such as this, and as fast as they are flattened they get up and keep belting away, and while the old experience is running for Sam the Gonoph and Jew Louie and Nubbsy Taylor and Benny South Street and old Liverlips early in the fight, the Harvards have youth in their favor.

Pretty soon the Harvards are knocking down Sam the Gonoph, then they start knocking down Nubbsy Taylor, and by and by they are knocking down Benny South Street and Jew Louie and Liverlips, and it is so much fun that the Harvards forget all about the goal posts. Of course as fast as Sam the Gonoph and his guys are knocked down they also get up, but the Harvards are too many for them, and they are getting an awful shellacking when the nine-foot guy who flattens me, and who is knocking down Sam the Gonoph so often he is becoming a great nuisance to Sam, sings out:

"Listen," he says, "these are game guys, even if they do go to Yale. Let us cease knocking them down," he says, "and give them a cheer."

So the Harvards knock down Sam the Gonoph and Nubbsy Taylor and Jew Louie and Benny South Street and old Liverlips just once more and then all the Harvards put their heads together and say rah-rah-rah, very loud, and go away, leaving the goal posts still standing, with our little doll still roosting on the cross-bar, although afterwards I hear some Harvards who are not in the fight get the posts at the other end of the field and

sneak away with them. But I always claim these posts
do not count.

Well, sitting there on the ground because he is too
tired to get up from the last knockdown, and holding
one hand to his right eye, which is closed tight, Sam the
Gonoph is by no means a well guy, and all around and
about him is much suffering among his crew. But our
little doll is hopping up and down chattering like a
jaybird and running between old Liverlips, who is
stretched out against one goal post, and Nubbsy Taylor, who is leaning up against the other, and she is
trying to mop the blood off their kissers with a handkerchief the size of a postage stamp.

Benny South Street is laying across Jew Louie and
both are still snoring from the last knockdown, and the
Bowl is now pretty much deserted except for the newspaper scribes away up in the press box, who do not
seem to realize that the Battle of the Century just comes
off in front of them. It is coming on dark, when all of
a sudden a guy pops up out of the dusk wearing white
spats and an overcoat with a fur collar, and he rushes
up to our little doll.

"Clarice," he says, "I am looking for you high and
low. My train is stalled for hours behind a wreck the
other side of Bridgeport, and I get here just after the
game is over. But," he says, "I figure you will be waiting somewhere for me. Let us hurry on to Hartford,
darling," he says.

Well, when he hears this voice, Sam the Gonoph
opens his good eye wide and takes a peek at the guy.

Then all of a sudden Sam jumps up and wobbles over to the guy and hits him a smack between the eyes. Sam is wobbling because his legs are not so good from the shellacking he takes off the Harvards, and furthermore he is away off in his punching as the guy only goes to his knees and comes right up standing again as our little doll lets out a screech and speaks as follows:

"Oo-oo!" she says. "Do not hit Elliot! He is not after our goal posts!"

"Elliot?" Sam the Gonoph says. "This is no Elliot. This is nobody but Gigolo Georgie. I can tell him by his white spats," Sam says, "and I am now going to get even for the pasting I take from the Harvards."

Then he nails the guy again and this time he seems to have a little more on his punch, for the guy goes down and Sam the Gonoph gives him the leather very good, although our little doll is still screeching, and begging Sam not to hurt Elliot. But of course the rest of us know it is not Elliot, no matter what he may tell her, but only Gigolo Georgie.

Well, the rest of us figure we may as well take a little something out of Georgie's hide, too, but as we start for him he gives a quick wiggle and hops to his feet and tears across the field, and the last we see of him is his white spats flying through one of the portals.

Now a couple of other guys come up out of the dusk, and one of them is a tall, fine-looking guy with a white mustache and anybody can see that he is some-body, and what happens but our little doll runs right into his arms and kisses him on the white mustache and calls him daddy and starts to cry more than somewhat, so I can see we lose our little doll then and there. And now the guy with the white mustache walks up to Sam the Gonoph and sticks out his duke and says as follows:

"Sir," he says, "permit me the honor of shaking the hand which does me the very signal service of chastising the scoundrel who just escapes from the field. And," he says, "permit me to introduce myself to you. I am J. Hildreth Van Cleve, president of the Van Cleve Trust. I am notified early today by Miss Peevy of my daughter's sudden departure from school, and we learn she purchases a ticket for New Haven. I at once suspect this fellow has something to do with it. Fortunately," he says, "I have these private detectives here keeping tab on him for some time, knowing my child's schoolgirl infatuation for him, so we easily trail him here. We are on the train with him, and arrive in time for your last little scene with him. Sir," he says, "again I thank you."

"I know who you are, Mr. Van Cleve," Sam the Gonoph says. "You are the Van Cleve who is down to his last forty million. But," he says, "do not thank me for putting the slug on Gigolo Georgie. He is a bum in spades, and I am only sorry he fools your nice little kid even for a minute, although," Sam says, "I figure she must be dumber than she looks to be fooled by such a guy as Gigolo Georgie."

"I hate him," the little doll says. "I hate him because he is a coward. He does not stand up and fight when he is hit like you and Liverlips and the others. I never wish to see him again."

"Do not worry," Sam the Gonoph says. "I will be too close to Gigolo Georgie as soon as I recover from my wounds for him to stay in this part of the country."

Well, I do not see Sam the Gonoph or Nubbsy Taylor or Benny South Street or Jew Louie or Liverlips for nearly a year after this, and then it comes on fall again and one day I get to thinking that here it is Friday and the next day the Harvards are playing the Yales a large football game in Boston.

I figure it is a great chance for me to join up with Sam the Gonoph again to hustle duckets for him for this game, and I know Sam will be leaving along about midnight with his crew. So I go over to the Grand Central station at such a time, and sure enough he comes along by and by, busting through the crowd in the station with Nubbsy Taylor and Benny South Street and Jew Louie and old Liverlips at his heels, and they seem very much excited.

"Well, Sam," I say, as I hurry along with them, "here I am ready to hustle duckets for you again, and I hope and trust we do a nice business."

"Duckets!" Sam the Gonoph says. "We are not hustling duckets for this game, although you can go with us, and welcome. We are going to Boston," he says, "to root for the Yales to kick hell out of the Harvards and we are going as the personal guests of Miss Clarice Van Cleve and her old man."

"Hold 'em, Yale!" old Liverlips says, as he pushes me to one side and the whole bunch goes trotting through the gate to catch their train, and I then notice they are all wearing blue feathers in their hats with a little white Y on these feathers such as college guys always wear at football games, and that moreover Sam the Gonoph is carrying a Yale pennant.

H. F. ELLIS (1907-   )

...is a Welshman by birth, an Oxfordian by education, and a Londoner by choice. On completing Oxford, he worked for one year as a schoolteacher; unlike the hapless Wentworth, Ellis soon left the profession. Since 1933 he has been a staff writer and editor for "Punch," the London humor magazine, and the Wentworth stories first appeared in that magazine.

No reader could mistake Ellis for an American. Not only the English preparatory school setting, but the dry, agile style and the sly, understated wit, mark his Wentworth stories as thoroughly—and delightfully —British.

1 teacher + 11 students = K. O. according to the

STATEMENT OF ARTHUR JAMES WENTWORTH, BACHELOR OF ARTS

MY NAME is Arthur James Wentworth, I am unmarried and I am by profession an assistant master at Burgrove Preparatory School, Wilminster. The Headmaster is the Reverend Gregory Saunders, M.A. He is known to the boys as the Squid—not necessarily, I think, a term of opprobrium. He is a classical scholar of moderate attainments, a generous employer and much given to the use of the expression "The School must come first, Wentworth." I attach no particular meaning to this remark.

At 11:15 on the morning of Saturday, July 8th, I entered Classroom 4 for the purpose of instructing Set IIIA in Algebra. There were present Anderson, Atkins, Clarke, Etheridge, Hillman, Hopgood II, Mason, Otterway, Sapoulos, Trench and Williamson. Heathcote, who has, I am told, a boil, was absent.

It should be explained that though I have given these names in the alphabetical order in which they appear in the school list, that is not the order in which the boys were sitting on this occasion. It is the custom at Burgrove for boys to sit according to their position in the previous week's mark-lists. Thus in the front row were seated Etheridge, a most promising mathematician, Hillman, Mason, Otterway and Clarke. Hopgood II, the boy whom I am now accused of assaulting, was in the middle of the second row. The third and last row was shared by Sapoulos, a Greek, and Atkins, a cretin. I do not think these facts have any bearing on anything that is to follow, but I give them for the sake of completeness.

"This morning," I remarked, taking up my Hall and Knight, "we will do problems," and I told them at once that if there was any more of that groaning they would do nothing but problems for the next month. It is my experience, as an assistant master of some years' standing, that if groaning is not checked immediately it may swell to enormous proportions. I make it my business to stamp on it.

Mason, a fair-haired boy with glasses, remarked when the groaning had died down that it would not be possible to do problems for the next month, and on being asked why not, replied that there were only three weeks more of term. This was true, and I decided to make no reply.

He then asked if he could have a plus mark for that. I said, "No, Mason, you may not," and, taking up my book and a piece of chalk, read out, "I am just half as old as my father and in twenty years I shall be five years older than he was twenty years ago. How old am I?" Atkins promptly replied, "Forty-two." I inquired of him how, unless he was gifted with supernatural powers, he imagined he could produce the answer without troubling to do any working out. He said, "I saw it in the School's Year-book." This stupid reply caused a great deal of laughter, which I suppressed.

I should have spoken sharply to Atkins, but at this moment I noticed that his neighbor Sapoulos, the Greek boy, appeared to be eating toffee, a practice which is forbidden at Burgrove during school hours. I ordered him to stand up. "Sapoulos," I said, "you are not perhaps quite used yet to our English ways, and I shall not punish you this time for your disobedience; but please understand that I will not have eating in my class. You did not come here to eat but to learn. If you try hard and pay attention I do not altogether despair of teaching you something, but if you do not wish to learn I cannot help you. You might as well go back to your own country."

Mason, without being given permission to speak, cried excitedly, "He can't, sir. Didn't you know? His father was chased out of Greece in a revolution or something. A big man with a black beard chased him for three miles and he had to escape in a small boat. It's true, sir. You ask him. Sapoulos got hit on the knee with a brick, didn't you, Sappy? And his grandmother —at least I think it was his grandmother——"

"That will do, Mason," I said. "Who threw that?"

I am not, I hope, a martinet, but I will not tolerate the throwing of paper darts or other missiles in my algebra set. Some of the boys make small pellets out of their blotting paper and flick them with their garters. This sort of thing has to be put down with a firm hand or work becomes impossible. I accordingly warned the boy responsible that another offense would mean a punishment. He had the impertinence to ask what sort of a punishment. I said that it would be a pretty stiff punishment, and if he wished to know more exact details he had only to throw another dart to find out. He thereupon threw another dart.

I confess that at this I lost patience and threatened to keep the whole set in during the afternoon if I had any more trouble. The lesson then proceeded.

It was not until I had completed my working out of the problem on the board that I realized I had worked on the assumption—of course ridiculous—that I was twice my father's age instead of half. This gave the false figure of minus ninety for my own age. Some boy said "Crikey!" I at once whipped round and demanded to know who had spoken. Otterway suggested that it might have been Hopgood II talking in his sleep. I was about to reprimand Otterway for impertinence when I realized that Hopgood actually was asleep and had in fact, according to Williamson, been asleep since the beginning of the period. Mason said, "He hasn't missed much anyway."

I then threw my Hall and Knight. It has been suggested that it was intended to hit Hopgood II. This is false. I never wake up sleeping boys by throwing books at them, as hundreds of old Burgrove boys will be able to testify. I intended to hit Mason, and it was by a mischance which I shall always regret that Hopgood was struck. I have had, as I told my Headmaster, a great deal to put up with from Mason, and no one who knows the boy blames me for the attempt to do him some physical violence. It is indeed an accepted maxim in the faculty lounge that physical violence is the only method of dealing with Mason which produces any results; to this the Headmaster some time ago added a rider that the boy be instructed to remove his spectacles before being assaulted. That I forgot to do this must be put down to the natural agitation of a mathematics master caught out in an error. But I blame myself for it.

I do not blame myself for the unfortunate stunning of Hopgood II. It was an accident. I did all I could for the boy when it was discovered (I think by Etheridge) that he had been rendered unconscious. I immediately summoned the Headmaster and we talked the matter over. We agreed that concealment was impossible and that I must give a full account of the circumstances to the police. Meanwhile the work of the school was to go on as usual; Hopgood himself would have wished it. The Headmaster added that in any case the School must come first.

I have made this statement after being duly cautioned, of my own free will and in the presence of witnesses. I have read it through three times with considerable satisfaction, and am prepared to state on oath that it is a true and full account of the circumstances leading up to the accident to Hopgood II. I wish only to add that the boy is now none the worse for the blow, and has indeed shown increased zeal for his studies since the occurrence.

JAMES THURBER (1894-1961)

... *was one of America's most versatile humorists. As a writer, he achieved fame with his essays, plays, and short stories. He was also one of the country's foremost cartoonists; Thurber's wistful, over-sized dogs have become a familiar symbol for bumbling eagerness.*

Throughout his career, Thurber was closely identified with the "New Yorker," and most of his writing and cartoons first appeared in that magazine. In the 1940's he became almost totally blind, but—to the amazement and delight of his admirers throughout the world—his output as a writer actually increased.

Thurber's humor has many faces and no one story can be singled out as typical. Among his most popular pieces are the gently humorous fairy tale, "Many Moons;" the slyly satiric "The Secret Life of Walter Mitty;" and the devastating parody of Henry James, "The Beast in the Dingle." "You Could Look It Up" represents Thurber at his most purely farcical.

A midget in the major leagues?

If you don't believe it,

YOU COULD LOOK IT UP

IT ALL BEGAN when we dropped down to C'lumbus, Ohio, from Pittsburgh to play a exhibition game on our way out to St. Louis. It was gettin' on into September, and though we'd been leadin' the league by six, seven games most of the season, we was now in first place by a margin you could 'a' got it into the eye of a thimble, bein' only a half a game ahead of St. Louis. Our slump had given the boys the leapin' jumps, and they was like a bunch a old ladies at a lawn fete with a thunderstorm comin' up, runnin' around snarlin' at each other, eatin' bad and sleepin' worse, and battin' for a team average of maybe .186. Half the time nobody'd speak to nobody else, without it was to bawl 'em out.

Squawks Magrew was managin' the boys at the time, and he was darn near crazy. They called him "Squawks" 'cause when things was goin' bad he lost his voice, or perty near lost it, and squealed at you like a little girl you stepped on her doll or somethin'. He yelled at everybody and wouldn't listen to nobody, without maybe it was me. I'd been trainin' the boys for ten year, and he'd take more lip from me than from anybody else. He knowed I was smarter'n him, anyways, like you're goin' to hear.

This was thirty, thirty-one year ago; you could look it up, 'cause it was the same year C'lumbus decided to call itself the Arch City, on account of a lot of iron arches with electric-light bulbs into 'em which stretched acrost High Street. Thomas Albert Edison sent 'em a telegram, and they was speeches and maybe even President Taft opened the celebration by pushin' a button. It was a great week for the Buckeye capital, which was why they got us out there for this exhibition game.

Well, we just lose a double-header to Pittsburgh, 11 to 5 and 7 to 3, so we snarled all the way to C'lumbus, where we put up at the Chittaden Hotel, still snarlin'. Everybody was tetchy, and when Billy Klinger took a sock at Whitey Cott at breakfast, Whitey throwed marmalade all over his face.

"Blind each other, whatta I care?" says Magrew. "You can't see nothin' anyways."

C'lumbus won the exhibition game, 3 to 2, whilst Magrew set in the dugout, mutterin' and cursin' like a fourteen-year-old Scotty. He bad-mouthed everybody on the ball club and he bad-mouthed everybody offa the ball club, includin' the Wright brothers, who, he claimed, had yet to build a airship big enough for any of our boys to hit it with a ball bat.

"I wisht I was dead," he says to me. "I wisht I was in heaven with the angels."

I told him to pull hisself together, 'cause he was drivin' the boys crazy, the way he was goin' on, sulkin' and bad-mouthin' and whinin'. I was older'n he was and smarter'n he was, and he knowed it. I was ten times smarter'n he was about this Pearl du Monville, first time I ever laid eyes on the little guy, which was one of the saddest days of my life.

Now, most people name of Pearl is girls, but this Pearl du Monville was a man if you could call a fella a man who was only thirty-four, thirty-five inches high. Pearl du Monville was a midget. He was part French and part Hungarian, and maybe even part Bulgarian or somethin'. I can see him now, a sneer on his little pushed-in pan, swingin' a bamboo cane and smokin' a big cigar. He had a gray suit with a big black check into it, and he had a gray felt hat with one of them rainbow-colored hatbands onto it, like the young fellas wore in them days. He talked like he was talkin' into a tin can, but he didn't have no foreign accent. He mighta been fifteen or he mighta been a hundred, you couldn't tell, Pearl du Monville.

After the game with C'lumbus, Magrew headed straight for the Chittaden bar—the train for St. Louis wasn't goin' for three, four hours—and there he set, drinkin' rye and talkin' to this bartender.

"How I pity me, brother," Magrew was tellin' this bartender. "How I pity me." That was alwuz his favorite tune. So he was settin' there, tellin' this bartender how heartbreakin' it was to be manager of a bunch of blind-folded circus clowns, when up pops this Pearl du Monville outa nowheres.

It give Magrew the leapin' jumps. He thought at first maybe the D.T.'s had come back on him; he claimed he'd had 'em once, and little guys had popped up all around him, wearin' red, white and blue hats.

"Go on, now!" Magrew yells. "Get away from me!"

But the midget clumb up on a chair acrost the table from Magrew and says, "I seen that game today, Junior, and you ain't got no ball club. What you got there, Junior," he says, "is a side show."

"Whatta ya mean, 'Junior'?" says Magrew touchin' the little guy to satisfy hisself he was real.

"Don't pay him no attention, mister," says the bartender. "Pearl calls everybody 'Junior,' 'cause it alwuz turns out he's a year older'n anybody else."

"Yeh?" says Magrew. "How old *is* he?"

"How old are you, Junior?" says the midget.

"Who, me? I'm fifty-three," says Magrew.

"Well, I'm fifty-four," says the midget.

Magrew grins and asts him what he'll have, and that was the beginnin' of their beautiful friendship, if you don't care what you say.

Pearl du Monville stood up on his chair and waved

his cane around and pretended like he was ballyhooin
for a circus. "Right this way, folks!" he yells. "Come
on in and see the greatest collection of freaks in the
world! See the armless pitchers, see the eyeless batters,
see the infielders with five thumbs!" and on and on
like that, feedin' Magrew gall and handin' him a laugh
at the same time, you might say.

You could hear him and Pearl du Monville hootin'
and hollerin' and singin' way up to the fourth floor
of the Chittaden, where the boys was packin' up.
When it come time to go to the station, you can
imagine how disgusted we was when we crowded
into the doorway of that bar and seen them two singin'
and goin' on.

"Well, well, well," says Magrew, lookin' up and
spottin' us. "Look who's here. . . . Clowns, this is Pearl
du Monville, a monseer of the old, old school. . . .
Don't shake hands with 'em, Pearl, 'cause their fingers
is made of chalk and would bust right off in your
paws," he says, and he starts guffawin' and Pearl starts
titterin' and we stand there given' 'em the iron eye, it
bein' the lowest ebb a ball-club manager'd got hisself
down to since the national pastime was started.

Then the midget begun givin' us the ballyhoo.
"Come on in!" he says, wavin' his cane. "See the leg-
less base runners, see the outfielders with the butter
fingers, see the southpaw with the arm of a chee-ild!"

Then him and Magrew begun to hoop and holler
and nudge each other till you'd 'a' thought this little
guy was the funniest guy than even Charlie Chaplin.

The fellas filed outa the bar without a word and went on up to the Union Depot, leavin' me to handle Magrew and his new-found crony.

Well, I got 'em outa there finely. I had to take the little guy along, 'cause Magrew had a holt onto him like a vise and I couldn't pry him loose.

"He's comin' along as masket," says Magrew, holdin' the midget in the crouch of his arm like a football. And come along he did, hollerin' and protestin' and beatin' at Magrew with his little fists.

"Cut it out, will ya, Junior?" the little guy kept whinin'. "Come on, leave a man loose, will ya, Junior?"

But Junior kept a holt onto him and begun yellin', "See the guys with the glass arm, see the guys with the cast-iron brains, see the infielders with the feet on their wrists!"

So it goes, right through the whole Union Depot, with people starin' and catcallin', and he don't put the midget down till he gets him through the gates.

"How'm I goin' to go along without no toothbrush?" the midget asts. "What'm I goin' to do without no other suit?" he says.

"Doc here," says Magrew, meanin' me—"doc here will look after you like you was his own son, won't you, doc?"

I give him the iron eye, and he finely got on the train and prob'ly went to sleep with his clothes on.

This left me alone with the midget. "Lookit," I says to him. "Why don't you go on home now? Come mornin', Magrew'll forget all about you. He'll prob'ly think you was somethin' he seen in a nightmare maybe. And he ain't goin' to laugh so easy in the mornin', neither," I says. "So why don't you go on home?"

"Nix," he says to me. "Skiddoo," he says, "twenty-three for you," and he tosses his cane up into the vestibule of the coach and clam'ers on up after it like a cat. So that's the way Pearl du Monville come to go to St. Louis with the ball club.

I seen 'em first at breakfast the next day, settin' opposite each other; the midget playin' Turkey in the Straw on a harmonium and Magrew starin' at his eggs and bacon like they was a uncooked bird with its feathers still on.

"Remember where you found this?" I says, jerkin' my thumb at the midget. "Or maybe you think they come with breakfast on these trains," i says, bein' a good hand at turnin' a sharp remark in them days.

The midget puts down the harmonium and turns on me. "Sneeze," he says, "your brains is dusty." Then he snaps a couple of drops of water at me from a tumbler. "Drown," he says, tryin' to make his voice deep.

Now, both them cracks is Civil War cracks, but you'd 'a' thought they was brand-new and the funniest than any crack Magrew'd ever heard in his whole life. He started hoopin' and hollerin', and the midget started hoopin' and hollerin', so I walked on away and set down with Bugs Courtney and Hank Metters, payin' no attention to this weak-minded Damon and Phidias acrost the aisle.

Well, sir, the first game with St. Louis was rained out, and there we was facin' a double-header next day. Like maybe I told you, we lose the last three double-headers we play, makin' maybe twenty-five errors in the six games, which is all right for the intimates of a school for the blind, but is disgraceful for the world's champions. It was too wet to go to the zoo, and Magrew wouldn't let us go to the movies, 'cause they flickered so bad in them days. So we just set around, stewin' and frettin'.

One of the newspaper boys come over to take a pitture of Billy Klinger and Whitey Cott shakin' hands—this reporter'd heard about the fight—and whilst they was standin' there, toe to toe, shakin' hands, Billy give a back lunge and a jerk, and throwed Whitey over his shoulder into a corner of the room, like a sack of salt. Whitey come back at him with a chair, and Bethlehem broke loose in that there room. The camera was tromped to pieces like a berry basket. When we finely got 'em pulled apart, I heard a laugh, and there was Magrew and the midget standin' in the door and givin' us the iron eye.

"Wrasslers," says Magrew, cold-like, "that's what I got for a ball club, Mr. du Monville, wrasslers—and not very good wrasslers at that, you ast me."

"A man can't be good at everythin'," says Pearl, "but he oughta be good at somethin'."

This set Magrew guffawin' again, and away they go, the midget taggin' along by his side like a hound dog and handin' him a fast line of so-called comic cracks.

When we went out to face that battlin' St. Louis club in a double-header the next afternoon, the boys was jumpy as tin toys with keys in their back. We lose the first game, 7 to 2, and are trailin', 4 to 0 when the second game ain't but ten minutes old. Magrew set there like a stone statue, speakin' to nobody. Then, in their half a the fourth, somebody singled to center and knocked in two more runs for St. Louis.

That made Magrew squawk. "I wisht one thing," he says. "I wisht I was manager of a old ladies' sewin' circus 'stead of a ball club."

"You are, Junior, you are," says a familyer and disagreeable voice that I am not happy to hear.

It was that Pearl du Monville again, poppin' up outa nowheres, swingin' his bamboo cane and smokin' a cigar that's three sizes too big for his face. By this time we'd finely got the other side out, and Hank Metters slithered a bat acrost the ground, and the midget had to jump to keep both his ankles from bein' broke.

I thought Magrew'd bust a blood vessel. "You hurt Pearl and I'll break your neck!" he yelled.

Hank muttered somethin' and went on up to the plate and struck out.

We managed to get a couple runs acrost in our half a the sixth, but they come back with three more in their half a the seventh, and this was too much for Magrew.

"Come on, Pearl," he says. "We're gettin' outa here."

"Where you think you're goin'?" I ast him.

"To the lawyer's again," he says cryptly.

"I didn't know you'd been to the lawyer's once, yet," I says.

"Which that goes to show how much you don't know," he says.

With that, they was gone, and I didn't see 'em the rest of the day, nor know what they was up to, which was a God's blessin'. We lose the nightcap, 9 to 3, and that puts us into second place plenty, and as low in our mind as a ball club can get.

The next day was a horrible day, like anybody that lived through it can tell you. Practice was just over and the St. Louis club was takin' the field, when I hears this strange sound from the stands. It sounds like the nervous whickerin' a horse gives when he smells somethin' funny on the wind. It was the fans ketchin' sight of Pearl du Monville, like you have prob'ly guessed. The midget had popped up onto the field all dressed up in a minacher club uniform, sox, cap, little letters sewed onto his chest, and all. He was swingin' a kid's bat and the only thing kept him from lookin' like a real ballplayer seen through the wrong end of a microscope was this cigar he was smokin'.

Bugs Courtney reached over and jerked it outa his mouth and throwed it away. "You're wearin' that suit on the playin' field," he says to him, severe as a judge. "You go insultin' it and I'll take you out to the zoo and feed you to the bears."

Pearl just blowed some smoke at him which he still has in his mouth.

Whilst Whitey was foulin' off four or five prior to strikin' out, I went on over to Magrew. "If I was as comic as you," I says, "I'd laugh myself to death," I says. "Is that any way to treat the uniform, makin' a mockery out of it?"

"It might surprise you to know I ain't makin' no mockery outa the uniform," says Magrew. "Pearl du Monville here has been made a bone-of-fida member of this so-called ball club. I fixed it up with the front office by long-distance phone."

"Yeh?" I says. "I can just hear Mr. Dillworth or Bart Jenkins agreein' to hire a midget for the ball club. I can just hear 'em." Mr. Dillworth was the owner of the club and Bart Jenkins was the secretary, and they never stood for no monkey business. "May I be so bold as to inquire," I says, "just what you told 'em?"

"I told 'em," he says, "I wanted to sign up a guy they ain't no pitcher in the league can strike him out."

"Uh-huh," I says, "and did you tell 'em what size of a man he is?"

"Never mind about that," he says. "I got papers on me, made out legal and proper, constitutin' one Pearl du Monville a bone-of-fida member of this former ball club. Maybe that'll shame them big babies into gettin' in there and swingin', knowin' I can replace any one of 'em with a midget, if I have a mind to. A St. Louis lawyer I seen twice tells me it's all legal and proper."

"A St. Louis lawyer would," I says, "seein' nothin' could make him happier than havin' you makin' a mockery outa this one-time baseball outfit," I says.

Well, sir, it'll all be there in the papers of thirty, thirty-one year ago, and you could look it up. The game went along without no scorin' for seven innings, and since they ain't nothin' much to watch but guys poppin' up or strikin' out, the fans pay most of their attention to the goin's-on of Pearl du Monville. He's out there in front a the dugout, turnin' handsprings, balancin' his bat on his chin, walkin' a imaginary line, and so on. The fans clapped and laughed at him, and he ate it up.

So it went up to the last a the eighth, nothin' to nothin', not more'n seven, eight hits all told, and no errors on neither side. Our pitcher gets the first two men out easy in the eighth. Then up come a fella name of Porter or Billings, or some such name, and he lammed one up against the tobacco sign for three bases. The next guy up slapped the first ball out into left for a base hit, and in come the fella from third for the only run of the ball game so far. The crowd yelled, the look a death come onto Magrew's face again, and even the midget quit his tomfoolin'. Their next man fouled out back a third, and we come up for our last bats like a bunch a schoolgirls steppin' into a pool of cold water. I was lower in my mind than I'd been since the day in nineteen-four when Chesbro throwed the wild pitch in the ninth inning with a man on third and lost the pennant for the Highlanders. I knowed something just as bad was goin' to happen, which shows I'm a clair-voyun, or was then.

When Gordy Mills hit out to second, I just closed

my eyes. I opened 'em up again to see Dutch Muller standin' on second, dustin' off his pants, him havin' got his first hit in maybe twenty time to the plate. Next up was Harry Loesing, battin' for our pitcher, and he got a base on balls, walkin' on a fourth one you could 'a' combed your hair with.

Then up come Whitey Cott, our lead-off man. He crotches down in what was prob'ly the most fearsome stanch in organized ball, but all he can do is pop out to short. That brung up Billy Klinger, with two down and a man on first and second. Billy took a cut at one you could 'a' knocked a plug hat offa this here Carnera with it, but then he gets sense enough to wait 'em out, and finely he walks, too, fillin' the bases.

Yes, sir, there you are; the tyin' run on third and the winnin' run on second, first a the ninth, two men down, and Hank Metters comin' to the bat. Hank was built like a Pope-Hartford and he couldn't run no faster'n President Taft, but he had five home runs to his credit for the season, and that wasn't bad in them days. Hank was still hittin' better'n anybody else on the ball club, and it was mighty heartenin', seein' him stridin' up towards the plate. But he never got there.

"Wait a minute!" yells Magrew, jumpin' to his feet. "I'm sendin' in a pinch hitter!" he yells.

You could 'a' heard a bomb drop. When a ball-club manager says he's sendin' in a pinch hitter for the best batter on the club, you know and I know and everybody knows he's lost his holt.

"They're goin' to be sendin' the funny wagon for

you, if you don't watch out," I says, grabbin' a holt of his arm.

But he pulled away and run out towards the plate, yellin', "Du Monville battin' for Metters!"

All the fellas begun squawlin' at once, except Hank, and he just stood there starin' at Magrew like he'd gone crazy and was claimin' to be Ty Cobb's grandma or somethin'. Their pitcher stood out there with his hands on his hips and a disagreeable look on his face, and the plate umpire told Magrew to go on and get a batter up. Magrew told him again Du Monville was battin' for Metters, and the St. Louis manager finely got the idea. It brung him outa his dugout, howlin' and bawlin' like he'd lost a female dog and her seven pups.

Magrew pushed the midget towards the plate and he says to him, he says, "Just stand up there and hold that bat on your shoulder. They ain't a man in the world can throw three strikes in there 'fore he throws four balls," he says.

"I get it, Junior," says the midget. "He'll walk me and force in the tyin' run!" And he starts on up to the plate as cocky as if he was Willie Keeler.

I don't need to tell you Bethlehem broke loose on that there ball field. The fans got onto their hind legs, yellin' and whistlin', and everybody on the field began wavin' their arms and hollerin' and shovin'. The plate umpire stalked over to Magrew like a traffic cop, waggin' his jaw and pointin' his finger, and the St. Louis manager kept yellin' like his house was on fire. When

Pearl got up to the plate and stood there, the pitcher slammed his glove down onto the ground and started stompin' on it, and they ain't nobody can blame him. He's just walked two normal-sized human bein's, and now here's a guy up to the plate they ain't more'n twenty inches between his knees and his shoulders.

The plate umpire called in the field umpire, and they talked a while, like a couple doctors seein' the bucolic plague or somethin' for the first time. Then the plate umpire come over to Magrew with his arms folded acrost his chest, and he told him to go on and get a batter up, or he'd forfeit the game to St. Louis. He pulled out his watch, but somebody batted it outa his hand in the scufflin', and I thought there'd be a free-for-all, with everybody yellin' and shovin' except Pearl du Monville, who stood up at the plate with his little bat on his shoulder, not movin' a muscle.

Then Magrew played his ace. I seen him pull some papers outa his pocket and show 'em to the plate um-pire. The umpire begun lookin' at 'em like they was bills for somethin' he not only never bought it, he never even heard of it. The other umpire studied 'em like they was a death warren, and all this time the St. Louis manager and the fans and the players is yellin' and hollerin'.

Well, sir, they fought about him bein' a midget, and they fought about him usin' a kid's bat, and they fought about where'd he been all season. They was eight or nine rule books brung out and everybody was thumbin' through 'em, tryin' to find out what it says about midgets, but it don't say nothin' about midgets, 'cause this was somethin' never'd come up in the history of the game before, and nobody'd ever dreamed about it, even when they has nightmares. Maybe you can't send no midgets in to bat nowadays, 'cause the old game's changed a lot, mostly for the worst, but you could then, it turned out.

The plate umpire finely decided the contrack papers was all legal and proper, like Magrew said, so he waved the St. Louis players back to their places and he pointed his finger at their manager and told him to quit hollerin' and get on back in the dugout. The manager says the game is percedin' under protest, and the umpire bawls, "Play ball!", over 'n' above the yellin' and booin', him havin' a voice like a hogcaller.

The St. Louis pitcher picked up his glove and beat at it with his fist six or eight times, and then got set on the mound and studied the situation. The fans realized he was really goin' to pitch to the midget, and they went crazy, hoopin' and hollerin' louder'n ever, and throwin' pop bottles and hats and cushions down onto the field. It took five, ten minutes to get the fans quieted down again, whilst our fellas that was on base set down on the bags and waited. And Pearl du Monville kept standin' up there with the bat on his shoulder, like he'd been told to.

So the pitcher starts studyin' the setup again, and you got to admit it was the strangest setup in a ball game since the players cut off their beards and begun wearin' gloves. I wisht I could call the pitcher's name

—it wasn't old Barney Pelty nor Nig Jack Powell nor Harry Howell. He was a big right-hander, but I can't call his name. You could look it up. Even in a crotchin' position, the ketcher towers over the midget like the Washington Monument.

The plate umpire tries standin' on his tiptoes, then he tries crotchin' down, and he finely gets hisself into a stanch nobody'd ever seen on a ball field before, kinda squattin' down on his hanches.

Well, the pitcher is sore as a old buggy horse in fly time. He slams in the first pitch, hard and wild, and maybe two foot higher'n the midget's head.

"Ball one!" hollers the umpire over 'n' above the racket, 'cause everybody is yellin' worsten ever.

The ketcher goes on out towards the mound and talks to the pitcher and hands him the ball. This time the big right-hander tries to undershoot, and it comes in a little closer, maybe no higher'n a foot, foot and a half above Pearl's head. It would 'a' been a strike with a human bein' in there, but the umpire's got to call it, and he does.

"Ball two!" he bellers.

The ketcher walks on out to the mound again, and the whole infield comes over and gives advice to the pitcher about what they'd do in a case like this, with two balls and no strikes on a batter that oughta be in a bottle of alcohol 'stead of up there at the plate in a big-league game between the teams that is fightin' for first place.

For the third pitch, the pitcher stands there flat-footed and tosses up the ball like he's playin' ketch with a little girl.

Pearl stands there motionless as a hitchin' post, and the ball comes in big and slow and high—high for Pearl, that is, it bein' about on a level with his eyes, or a little higher'n a grown man's knees.

They ain't nothin' else for the umpire to do, so he calls, "Ball three!"

Everybody is onto their feet, hoopin' and hollerin', as the pitcher sets to throw ball four. The St. Louis manager is makin' signs and faces like he was a con-torturer, and the infield is givin' the pitcher some more advice about what to do this time. Our boys who was on base stick right onto the bag, runnin' no risk of bein' nipped for the last out.

Well, the pitcher decides to give him a toss again, seein' he come closer with that than with a fast ball. They ain't nobody ever seen a slower ball throwed. It came in big as a balloon and slower'n any ball ever throwed before in the major leagues. It come right in over the plate in front of Pearl's chest, lookin' prob'ly big as a full moon to Pearl. They ain't never been a minute like the minute that followed since the United States was founded by the Pilgrim grandfathers.

Pearl du Monville took a cut at that ball, and he hit it! Magrew give a groan like a poleaxed steer as the ball rolls out in front a the plate into fair territory.

"Fair ball!" yells the umpire, and the midget starts runnin' for first, still carryin' that little bat, and makin' maybe ninety foot an hour. Bethlehem breaks loose on that ball field and in them stands. They ain't never been nothin' like it since creation was begun.

The ball's rollin' slow, on down towards third, goin' maybe eight, ten foot. The infield comes in fast and our boys break from their bases like hares in a brush-fire. Everybody is standin' up, yellin' and hollerin', and Magrew is tearin' his hair outa his head, and the midget is scamperin' for first with all the speed of one of them little dashhounds carryin' a satchel in his mouth.

The ketcher gets to the ball first, but he boots it on out past the pitcher's box, the pitcher fallin' on his face tryin' to stop it, the shortstop sprawlin' after it full length and zaggin' it on over towards the second base-man, whilst Muller is scorin' with the tyin' run and Loesing is roundin' third with the winnin' run. Ty Cobb could 'a' made a three-bagger outa that bunt, with everybody fallin' over theirself tryin' to pick the ball up. But Pearl is still maybe fifteen, twenty feet from the bag, toddlin' like a baby and yeepin' like a trapped rabbit, when the second baseman finely gets a holt o' that ball and slams it over to first. The first baseman ketches it and stomps on the bag, the base umpire waves Pearl out, and there goes your old ball game, the craziest ball game ever played in the history of the organized world.

Their players start runnin' in, and then I see Ma-grew. He starts after Pearl, runnin' faster'n any man ever run before. Pearl sees him comin' and runs behind the base umpire's legs and gets a holt onto 'em. Ma-

grew comes up, pantin' and roarin', and him and the
midget plays ring-around-a-rosy with the umpire, who
keeps shovin' at Magrew with one hand and tryin' to
slap the midget loose from his legs with the other.

Finely Magrew ketches the midget, who is still
yeepin' like a stuck sheep. He gets holt of that little
guy by both his ankles and starts whirlin' him round
and round his head like Magrew was a hammer
thrower and Pearl was the hammer. Nobody can stop
him without gettin' their head knocked off so everybody just stands there and yells. Then Magrew lets the
midget fly. He flies on out towards second, high and
fast, like a human home run, headed for the soap sign
in center field.

Their shortstop tries to get to him, but he can't
make it, and I knowed the little fella was goin' to bust
to pieces like a dollar watch on a asphalt street when
he hit the ground. But it so happens their center fielder
is just crossin' second, and he starts runnin' back, tryin'
to get under the midget, who had took to spiralin'
like a football 'stead of turnin' head over foot, which
give him more speed and more distance.

I know you never seen a midget ketched, and you
prob'ly never ever seen one throwed. To ketch a
midget that's been throwed by a heavy-muscled man
and is flyin' through the air, you got to run under him
and with him and pull your hands and arms back and
down when you ketch him, to break the compact of his
body, or you'll bust him in two like a match-stick. I see
Bill Lange and Willie Keeler and Tris Speaker make

some wonderful ketches in my day, but I never seen nothin' like that center fielder. He gets back and back and still further back and he pulls that midget down outa the air like he was liftin' a sleepin' baby from a cradle. They wasn't a bruise onto him, only his face was the color of cat's meat and he ain't got no air in his chest. In his excitement, the base umpire, who was runnin' back with the center fielder when he ketched Pearl, yells, "Out!" and that give hysterics to the Bethlehem which was ragin' like Niagry on that ball field.

Everybody was hoopin' and hollerin' and yellin' and runnin', with the fans swarmin' onto the field, and the cops tryin' to keep order, and some guys laughin' and some of the women fans cryin', and six or eight of us holdin' onto Magrew to keep him from gettin' at that midget and finishin' him off. Some of the fans picks up the St. Louis pitcher and the center fielder, and starts carryin' 'em around on their shoulders, and they was the craziest goin's-on knowed to the history of organized ball on this side of the 'Lantic Ocean.

I seen Pearl du Monville strugglin' in the arms of a lady fan with a ample bosom, who was laughin' and cryin' at the same time, and him beatin' at her with his little fists and bawlin' and yellin'. He clawed his way loose finely and disappeared in the forest of legs which made that ball field look like it was Coney Island on a hot summer's day.

That was the last I ever seen of Pearl du Monville. I never seen hide nor hair of him from that day to this, and neither did nobody else. He just vanished into the thin of the air, as the fella says. He was ketched for the final out of the ball game and that was the end of him, just like it was the end of the ball game, you might say, and also the end of our losin' streak, like I'm goin' to tell you.

That night we piled onto a train for Chicago, but we wasn't snarlin' and snappin' any more. No, sir, the ice was finely broke and a new spirit come into that ball club. The old zip came back with the disappearance of Pearl du Monville, and 'fore long Magrew was laughin' with us. He got a human look onto his pan again, and he quit whinin' and complainin' and wishin' he was in heaven with the angels.

Well, sir, we wiped up that Chicago series, winnin' all four games, and makin' seventeen hits in one of 'em. Funny thing was, St. Louis was so shook up by that last game with us, they never did hit their stride again. Their center fielder took to misjudgin' everything that come his way, and the rest a the fellas followed suit, the way a club'll do when one guy blows up.

'Fore we left Chicago, I and some of the fellas went out and bought a pair of them little baby shoes, which we had 'em golded over and give 'em to Magrew for a souvenir, and he took it all in good spirit. Whitey Cott and Billy Klinger made up and was fast friends again, and we hit our home lot like a ton of dynamite and they was nothin' could stop us from then on.

I don't recollect things as clear as I did thirty, forty years ago. I can't read no fine print no more, and the

only person I got to check with on the golden days of
the national pastime, as the fella says, is my friend, old
Milt Kline, over in Springfield, and his mind ain't as
strong as it once was.

He gets Rube Waddell mixed up with Rube Mar-
quard, for one thing, and anybody does that oughta be
put away where he won't bother nobody. So I can't
tell you the exact margin we win the pennant by.
Maybe it was two and a half games, or maybe it was
three and a half. But it'll all be there in the newspapers
and record books of thirty, thirty-one year ago and, like
I was sayin', you could look it up.

WILLIAM J. LEDERER (1912-   )

. . . is an authority on Southeast Asia. He made head-lines and caused an international stir with his fictional account of how the people of Asia react to American statesmanship. The Ugly American *was eventually made into a film.*

Lederer's writing stems largely from his own experi-ence as a Captain in the U.S. Navy. He has chron-icled his rise from enlisted man to ranking officer in Ensign O'Toole and Me, *first published as a novel in 1957. The O'Toole saga became a television series in 1962.* Sarkhan *was published in 1965.*

Everyone wanted to know where

THE SKIPPER'S
PINK PANTIES

came from

WHEN CAPTAIN BURKE received orders to China I pulled strings to go with him. No luck. The Bureau of Navigation said "—Ensign Lederer needs more seasoning before a tour in the Orient."

The day Captain Burke left, we nearly cried. Especially as the *Fortune's* new skipper, Captain "Bullet Head" Poindexter, didn't measure up to the recent standard. A huge man with a small head and a high-pitched voice, he made it clear from the start that everything in the ship revolved about him.

As a shiphandler and a tactician, Captain Poindexter carried out his duties in a sound manner. In his human relations he fell into an error too common to military men: he believed because he was a military expert that, ipso facto, he also had a greater knowledge of philosophy, art, sex, philology, etc., than any person beneath him in rank.

Captain Poindexter enjoyed stating a theory at mealtime and then, with big words, ramming it down the throats of his, in his opinion, untutored junior officers. He usually memorized articles in the encyclopedia before coming to the wardroom.

When he learned that I was the ship's radical—that is, a believer in the New Deal—Captain Poindexter (an Old Guard Republican) addressed his mealtime discussions in my general direction. Before many months went by I violently disputed the Old Man's theories. Frankly, his mind operated slowly; and ruining his theories was easy. Often I embarrassed him; the more I argued the more annoyed he became. It became a fad with me to foul up the captain's pompousness, and I used every sophistry and dirty trick in the book.

For example, once, after a lengthy wrangle, the Captain angrily concluded with his clincher argument. "Irregardless, Lederer, the fact remains that Americans are better farmers than Chinese. Max Store in his book, *"The Orient in Rebellion,* clearly proves this."

"Captain," I said smugly, "I'm afraid there's no such word as irregardless. And as for Mr. Store, he never saw a Chinese farmer in his life. No one who knows *anything* about the Orient would accept a word—."

The Old Man exploded. "I'm sick and tired of your shyster arguments and sharp practices. Now listen to me. I don't want you ever to open your mouth in this wardroom again. Do you understand? That's an order! As long as I'm commanding officer, you keep your mouth shut. Shut tight."

"Aye, aye, sir."

"Except," continued the Skipper, "if I tell a joke. And then, by God, you lean back in your chair and laugh and laugh and laugh."

We ensigns all agreed that I won that round.

I soon found out that actually I had lost it. Captain Poindexter wasn't kidding. The next day, when I made a remark at lunch, he ordered me to my room for two days for failing to carry out his orders. A week later he showed me the first draft of my fitness report.

"Although this young officer carries out his duties well," the report read, "he has an inclination to be un-cooperative with the commanding officer. He has applied for duty in China. His commanding officer has recommended that this not be approved until Ensign Lederer acquires more social maturity. His perspective on respect due a senior officer is slightly warped."

The fitness report, if sent in, could easily ruin my career. Furthermore, upon thinking the thing over, I concluded that the Captain had a lot of truth on his side. I decided to woo the guy scientifically.

I bought *How to Win Friends and Influence People* and read it carefully. It seemed that the way to gain back the Old Man's friendship was to ask him his advice on personal questions and, later, when the opportunity arose, let him beat me in a discussion.

Meanwhile, I got into a bit of trouble somewhere

else. I told a young lady at a dance that her petticoat was showing; she, having a couple of drinks under her girdle, felt offended and slapped me. She told an admiral that I had been fresh with her. He reprimanded me.

Here, I thought, was the time to seek Captain Poindexter's counsel.

The next morning, at breakfast, I brought up the problem.

"Captain, sir, I'm in some personal trouble and would very much appreciate your advice on the matter."

There came a long silence, during which time I didn't know whether he'd send me to my room again for talking, or help me out.

"What's your trouble?" he said finally.

"Sir," I said, dropping my eyes and trying to look contrite, "last night I went to a dance. I noticed that one girl's petticoat hung down. I went up to her politely, trying to be helpful, and told—"

"Petticoat!" roared the skipper looking up from his pork chop and scrambled eggs. "Did I hear you say petticoat?"

"Yes, sir."

He put his hand to his head and opened his mouth as if he had seen a ghost. "Petticoat! You mean a slip, man, a slip! Women haven't worn petticoats for thirty years."

I said nothing.

"Do you know the difference between a petticoat and

a slip?"

"No, sir."

"Good heavens! Can there be an officer on my ship as dumb as that?" The captain warmed to his subject.

"Do you know what a redingtoe is?" he asked.

"No, sir."

"What's a dirndl?"

"I don't know, sir."

"A jabot?"

"I don't know, sir."

"An officer on my ship!" moaned the captain. "Is it possible?"

The Old Man waved for Abe to bring him another pork chop. While waiting for it, he continued working me over.

"Mr. Lederer, are you familiar with Article 912, U.S. Navy Regulations?"

"No, sir. But I'll look it up."

"Don't bother. I'll tell you—it says that I, as your commanding officer, am responsible for your professional training. And, by gad, mister, I'm going to see that the Regulations are carried out."

"I appreciate it, sir."

He continued. "No one's going to say I neglected my duty. Being a good officer is more than conning a ship and shooting the guns. It also embraces knowing your way around in society."

The skipper's pork chop arrived.

"It's evident to me," said the Old Man, "that you haven't had much experience with women. A petticoat!"

"I'll admit I'm pretty shy, sir."

"Shy! You just haven't been around. How old are you?"

"Twenty-six, sir."

"And you don't know a blessed thing about undergarments. Lederer—"

"No, sir. I'm pretty ignorant on that subject—."

"I want you to go out with a woman over this weekend," Captain Poindexter chuckled. His chuckle turned into a belly laugh. "Oh ho! What a situation. Ho, ohhh, ho!"

"Aye, aye, sir," I said, smiling.

"Mister, this is no joking matter. I'm ordering you to take a woman out this week-end."

"Aye, aye, sir."

"And bring back a hunk of her underwear to prove it. Bring back her step-ins. You know what step-ins are, I hope."

"Yes, sir."

"Very well, Mister. Go ashore in the first liberty boat and carry out your orders. Good hunting, son," he said, running into another belly laugh.

That afternoon, after going ashore, I looked up a married classmate and explained the problem. His wife bought a cheap pair of pink step-ins for me. I sprinkled some sand on them, wrapped them up in a damp towel, and threw the bundle in the back of my car. I would bring the panties out to the ship on Monday.

However, the next evening, Sunday, I turned the

matter over in my mind and decided that it wouldn't be dignified showing the underclothes on the ship in front of my shipmates. I telephoned the Captain's home to ask him if I could bring my trophy to his house.

Mrs. Poindexter answered.

"No, Mr. Lederer, the Captain isn't home. He went fishing over the week-end. Can I take a message?"

"No, ma'am, it's nothing important, thank you."

It occurred to me that the Captain might appreciate my being nice to his wife, so I invited her to come to the open-air movies with me at the Strand, a couple of miles down the beach from Coronado. She accepted. We saw the late showing of *The Baroness and the Butler* and I left her her at her home about 11 P.M.

"When you see the Captain tonight, Mrs. Poindexter," I said as I left her porch, "please tell him I got what he ordered. He'll know what I mean."

"He won't be back this evening. He won't be back until the morning and he's going straight out to the ship."

Leaving the Captain's home, I went to the club and turned in, returning to the *Fortune* at 0745 the next morning, clutching the towel with my precious panties wrapped up in it.

The officer of the deck stopped me as I reached the main deck.

"The Old Man left word to send you below pronto. He's got a mob down there."

"A mob?"

"Yeh, looks like the skippers and execs from every ship in the squadron came over to inspect your loot. The Old Man's putting you on the spot, too. He's told them the whole story about ordering you to go out with a gal and bring back her pants. Now you better hurry; it's only ten minutes until quarters."

"He's done me dirt," I muttered on my way to the wardroom.

The officer of the deck hadn't exaggerated. The place was so jammed with senior officers that I couldn't get beyond the entrance.

The buzz of many voices stopped as I appeared.

"Well, sir," the Old Man greeted me sternly, "have you carried out your orders?"

I took the pink garment from the towel and held it up.

Cheers resounded throughout the wardroom.

"Gentlemen," said the Captain, "I'm proud to announce that Ensign Lederer has carried his mission to a successful conclusion, as you can see. His courage, resourefulness, determination and, may I say, good taste, reflect credit upon himself and upon the naval service—."

"Speech! Speech!"

"—And now, perhaps, we can persuade him to tell us just how he obtained such a beautiful and useful piece of apparel. Yes, tell us about it, son."

More cheers.

I hesitated.

"Come on, Mister," said Captain Poindexter, "speak

up."

"Aw gosh," I said, "there was nothing to it. I just carried out your orders."

Everyone shouted.

"You seen your duty and you done it all right!"

"You can come over to my ship as supply officer any time you want," said one of the skippers laughing and enthusiastically pumping my hand.

"Give us the pitch on your technique."

I didn't know what to do; but here, at least, was my opportunity to show the Old Man that I was cooperative.

I looked at him. He nodded for me to go ahead.

"Well, if you insist," I said, "it was like this. Last night we were driving along the beach—"

I paused for effect.

A half dozen destroyer captains hung on every syllable. I decided to lay it on thick.

"There was a big moon." I continued. "The surf thundered on the beach, and yellow lights twinkled from nearby cottages. The top of the car was down and the summer breeze blew through my companion's hair—."

"Well," laughed someone, "at last we've got the girl in the picture."

Captain Poindexter held up his hand.

"Give him a chance, he'll tell us the story."

The situation worried me. What I had intended as a funny yarn looked as if it might get out of hand. I glanced at my watch; it was three minutes until morning quarters. If I could stall for just that long, then the meeting would break up of its own accord. I continued.

" 'What a wonderful night,' my girl said to me, 'let's stop for a while and look at the moon. We have plenty of time.' "

My audience laughed. Only a minute and a half to go until quarters.

"I stopped the car," I went on. "We put our heads back and looked at the big silvery moon. It seemed as if it were about to drop into the ocean—."

"Never mind the build-up," called the heckler. "Let's get down to business. How did you get the drawers?"

"What's the babe's name and telephone number?" asked another.

I bit my lip.

"Go ahead," said Captain Poindexter, "give us the dope on this little rendezvous. You're among shipmates. Let your hair down and tell all."

The wardroom buzzer sounded.

Hopefully I thought that it might be the signal for morning quarters. But no, thirty seconds to go yet. The buzzer gave notice that the squadron commodore (a grand guy, my old instructor at Annapolis) had come aboard. Captain Poindexter made a move to meet him, but before he could reach the passageway the commodore descended the ladder leading to the wardroom. Seeing me standing apparently alone in the entrance, he greeted me.

"Good morning, Lederer; hey, didn't I see you driving on the beach about midnight last night with—"

He paused to catch his breath, and everyone in the wardroom nearly fell out of his shoes waiting for the rest of the sentence.

"—with Mrs. Poindexter? That was Mrs. Poindexter, wasn't it?"

I didn't say anything. The blood rushed to my head and I felt like running and hiding in the bilges. The commodore stood there waiting for an answer.

"Yes, sir," I answered, "that was Mrs. Poindexter."

Captain Poindexter opened his mouth a few times but no sound came out.

I twisted my cap in my hands.

Slowly, one by one, the officers from other ships found excuses for leaving. Quarters sounded. Frantically I fumbled through my pockets for the sales slip on the panties. Finally, I found it and thrust it into the Captain's hand. He looked at it for a few seconds and went into his cabin.

He didn't talk much to anyone for a while, and never referred to the incident. Two days later he called me into his cabin.

"Do you still want to go to China?"

"Yes, sir."

"That's all," he said, nodding toward the door.

The following Monday I received dispatch orders to report to the Commander-in-Chief, Asiatic Fleet, Shanghai, China.

LUDWIG BEMELMANS (1898-1962)

... was a noted writer of humorous stories, essays, and novels, as well as a painter of considerable stature.

He is perhaps best known as the author and illustrator of "Madeline," a delightful tale in verse set in a Paris girls' school. Intended for children, "Madeline" has amused readers of all ages since its publication in 1939.

Bemelmans was an extraordinarily energetic and exuberant man. Sheer love of living—and of people—pervades all his writings. The charm of the semi-autobiographical "Little Bit and the America" derives equally from Bemelmans' high spirits and from his obvious and endearing tenderness toward his daughter.

Dogs are dogs, ships are ships, but

LITTLE BIT AND
THE "AMERICA"

are just plain trouble!

"LOOK, WHAT A lovely day we have for sailing," I said, pointing my pen toward the lit-up greenery outside the open window. The birds sang in the trees, and the sun shone on a deck of brightly colored luggage tags which I was filling out. Under *"S.S. America"* I had carefully lettered my name, and I answered the gay question of "Destination?" with "Cherbourg."

I was about to fill out a new tag when I noticed Barbara's silence. She was standing at the window, staring at me. I saw clearly the symptoms of wanting something, symptoms long known to me and always the same. I remembered that the day before she had said something about a dog, but I had been called away before I could talk about it at length.

For the most part, Barbara is a sweet and normal child; when she wants something, she changes. The child is then under great stress. A trembling of the lower lip precedes the filling of the beautiful eyes with tears. I am allowed to see these hopeless eyes for a moment, and then, as a spotlight moves from one place to another, she averts her gaze and slowly turns, folds her arms, and looks into the distance, or if there is no distance, at the wall. The crisis is approaching. She swallows, but her throat is constricted; finally, with the urgency of a stammerer, and with her small hands clenched, she manages to convey a few dry words. The small voice is like a cold trumpet. The last word is a choking sound. There is a long, cold silence.

On the morning of sailing I recognized the first stage of this painful condition that overcomes her from time to time. I could tell it by her eyes, her mouth, the position she stood in, the peculiar angles of her arms and legs. She was twisted in an unhappy pose of indecision. Not that she didn't know precisely what she wanted: she was undecided about how to broach the subject.

After the tears, the gaze into the distance, the silence, Barbara blurted out, "You promised I could have a dog."

I steeled myself and answered, "Yes, when we get back from Europe you can have a dog."

An answer like that is worse than outright no. The mood of "I wish I was dead" descended on Barbara. She stared coldly out of the window, and then she turned and limply dragged herself down the corridor to her room, where she goes at times of crisis. She closed the door not by slamming it, but with a terrible, slow finality. One can see from the corridor how she lets go of the handle inside—in unspeakably dolorous fashion: slowly the handle rises, and there is the barely audible click of the mechanism. There is then the cutting off of human relations, a falling off of appetite, and nothing in the world of joy or disaster matters.

Ordinarily the comatose state lasts for weeks. In this case, however, Barbara was confronted with a deadline, for the ship was sailing at five that afternoon and it was now eleven in the morning. I usually break down after three or four weeks of resistance. The time limit for this operation was five hours.

She decided at first to continue with standard practice, the manual of which I know as well as I do the alphabet.

From the door at the end of the corridor came the sound of heartbreaking sobs. Normally these sobs last for a good while, and then, the crisis ebbing off, there follows an hour or two of real or simulated sleep, in which she gathers strength for renewed efforts. This time, however, the sobs were discontinued ahead of schedule and were followed by a period of total silence, which I knew was taken up with plotting at the speed of calculating machinery. This took about ten minutes. As the door had closed, so it opened again, and fatefully and slowly, as the condemned walk to their place of execution, the poor child, handkerchief in hand, dragged along the corridor past my room into the kitchen. I never knew until that morning that the pouring of milk into a glass could be a bitter and hopeless thing to watch.

I am as hardened against the heartbreak routine as a coroner is to post-mortems. I can be blind to tears and deaf to the most urgent pleading. I said, "Please be reasonable. I promise you that the moment we get back you can have a dog."

I was not prepared for what followed—the new slant, the surprise attack.

She leaned against the kitchen doorjamb and drank the last of the milk. Her mouth was ringed with white. She said in measured and accusing tones, "You read in the papers this morning what they did in Albany."

"I beg your pardon?"

"They passed a law that all institutions like the A.S.P.C.A. are to be forced to turn dogs over to hospitals, for vivisection—and you know what will happen. They'll get her and then they'll cut her open and sew her up again over and over until she's dead."

"What has that got to do with me?"

"It has to do with the dog you promised me."

"What dog?"

"The dog that Frances wants to give me."

Frances is a red-headed girl who goes to school with Barbara.

"I didn't know Frances had a dog."

Barbara raised her eyebrows. "You never listen," she said, and as if talking to an idiot and with weary gestures she recited, "Poppy, I told you all about it a dozen times. Doctor Lincoln, that's Frances' father, is going to Saudi Arabia to work for an oil company, and he had to sign a paper agreeing not to take a dog, because it seems the Arabs don't like dogs. So the dog has to be got rid of. So Doctor Lincoln said to Frances, 'If you don't get rid of her, I will.' Now you know how doctors are—they have no feelings whatever for animals. He'll give her to some hospital for experiments."

I resumed filling out baggage tags. When I hear the word "dog" I see in my mind a reasonably large animal of no particular breed, uncertain in outline, like a Thurber dog, and with a rough, dark coat. This image was hovering about when I asked, "What kind of a dog is it?"

"Her name is Little Bit."

"What?"

"Little *BIT*—that's her name. She's the dearest, sweetest, snow-white, itsey-bitsy tiny little toy poodle you have ever seen. Can I have her, please?"

I almost let out a shrill bark.

"Wait till you see her and all the things she's got— a special little wicker bed with a mattress, and a dish with her picture on it, and around it is written 'Always faithful' in French. You see, Poppy, they got Little Bit in Paris last year, and she's the uniquest, sharpest little dog you've ever seen, and naturally she's house-broken, and Frances says she's not going to give her to anybody but me."

I was playing for time. I would have settled for a

Corgi, a Yorkshire, a Weimaraner, even a German boxer or a Mexican hairless, but Little Bit was too much. I knew that Doctor Lincoln lived some thirty miles out of the city, and that it would be impossible to get the dog to New York before the ship sailed.

"Where is the dog now?" I asked with faked interest.

"She'll be here any minute, Poppy. Frances is on the way now—and oh, wait till you see, she has the cutest little boots for rainy weather, and a cashmere sweater, sea green, and several sets of leashes and collars—you won't have to buy a thing."

"All right," I said, "you can have the dog. We'll put it in a good kennel until we return."

The symptoms, well known and always the same, returned again. The lower lip trembled. "Kennel," she said—and there is no actress on stage or screen who could have weighted this word with more reproach and sheer, unadulterated, heartbroken misery.

"Yes, kennel," I said and filled out the baggage tag for my typewriter.

"Poppy—" she started, but I got up and said, "Now look, Barbara, the ship leaves in a few hours, and to take a dog aboard you have to get a certificate from a veterinary, and reserve a place for him, and buy a ticket."

To my astonishment, Barbara smiled indulgently. "Well, if that's all that's bothering you—first of all, we're going to France; the French, unlike the English, have no quarantine for dogs, and they don't even ask for a health certificate. Second, you can make all the arrangements for the dog's passage on board ship, after it sails. Third, there is plenty of room in the kennels. I know all this because Frances and I went down to the U. S. Lines and got the information day before yesterday."

I stared into distance. At such times I feel a great deal for the man who's going to marry Barbara. With all hope failing I said, "But we'll have to get a traveling bag or something to put the dog in."

"She has a lovely traveling bag with her name lettered on it, 'Little Bit.' "

The name stung like a whip. "All right then." I wrote an extra baggage tag to be attached to the dog's bag.

Barbara wore the smug smile of success. "Wait till you see her," she said and ran out of the room. In a moment she returned with Frances, who, I am sure, had been sitting there waiting all the while. The timing was perfect.

Little Bit had shoebutton eyes and patent-leather nose and a strawberry-colored collar; she was fluffy from the top of her head to her shoulders and then shorn like a miniature Persian lamb. At the end of a stub of a tail was a puff of fluff, and other puffs on the four legs. She wore a pale blue ribbon, and a bell on the collar. I thought that if she were cut open most probably sawdust would come out.

A real dog moves about a room and sniffs its way into corners. It inspects furniture and people, and makes notes of things. Little Bit stood with a cock-sparrow stiffness on four legs as static as her stare. She was picked up and brought over to me. I think she knew exactly what I thought of her, for she lifted her tiny lip on the left side of her face over her mouse teeth and sneered. She was put down, and she danced on stilts, with the motion of a mechanical toy, back to Frances.

I was shown the traveling bag, which was like one of the pocketbooks that WAC colonels carry.

"We don't need that tag," said Barbara. "I'll carry her in this. Look." The pocketbook, which had a circular opening with a wire screen on each end for breathing purposes, was opened; Little Bit jumped into it, and it was closed. "You see, she won't be any bother whatever."

The bag was opened again. With a standing jump Little Bit hurdled the handles of the bag and stalked toward me. Tilting her head a little, she stood looking up, and then she again lifted her lip over her small fangs.

"Oh, look, Barbara!" said Frances. "Little Bit likes your father—she's smiling at him."

I had an impulse to sneer back, but I took the baggage tags and began to attach them to the luggage. Then I left the room, for Frances showed signs of crisis; her eyes were filling, and the heartbreak was too much for me. Little Bit was less emotional. She ate a hearty meal from her *Toujours fidèle* dish and inspected the house, tinkling about with the bell that hung from her collar.

It was time to go to the boat. The luggage was taken to a taxi, and Little Bit hopped into her bag. On the way I thought about the things I had forgotten to take care of, and also about Little Bit. It is said that there are three kinds of books that are always a success: a book about a doctor, a book about Lincoln, and a book about a dog. Well, here was Doctor Lincoln's dog, but it didn't seem to hold the elements of anything except chagrin. I wondered if Lincoln had ever had a dog, or a doctor, or if Lincoln's doctor had had a dog. I wondered if that side of Lincoln, perhaps the last remaining side, had been investigated as yet or was still open.

We arrived with Doctor Lincoln's dog at the customs barrier, and our passports were checked. The baggage was brought aboard. In our cabin we found some friends waiting. Frances and Barbara, with Little Bit looking out of her bag, inspected the ship. The gong sounded, and the deck steward sang out, "All ashore that's going ashore!" The passengers lined up to wave their farewells. The last of those that were going ashore slid down the gangplank. Good-by, good-by— and then the engine bells sounded below, and the tugs moaned and hissed, and the ship backed out into the river.

There are few sights in the world as beautiful as a trip down the Hudson and out to sea, especially at dusk. I was on deck until we passed the Ambrose Lightship, and then I went down to the cabin.

Little Bit was lying on a blotter, on the writing desk,

and watching Barbara's hand. Barbara was already writing a letter to Frances, describing the beauty of travel and Little Bit's reactions. "Isn't she the best traveling dog we've ever had, Poppy?"

The cabins aboard the *America* are the only ones I have ever been in that don't seem to be aboard ship. They are large—more like rooms in a country home—a little chintzy in decoration, and over the portholes are curtains. In back of these one suspects screened doors that lead out to a porch and a Connecticut lawn rather than to the Atlantic Ocean.

I put my things in place and changed to a comfortable jacket. I said, "I guess I better go up and get this dog business settled."

"It's all attended to, Poppy. I took care of it," said Barbara and continued writing.

"Well, then you'd better take her upstairs to the kennels. It's almost dinnertime."

"She doesn't have to go to the kennels."

"Now, look, Barbara—"

"See for yourself, Poppy. Just ring for the steward, or let me ring for him."

"Yes, sir," said the steward, smiling.

"Is it all right for the dog to stay in the cabin?" I asked. The steward had one of the most honest and kind faces I have ever seen. He didn't fit on a ship either. He was more like a person that works around horses, or a gardener. He had bright eyes and squint lines, a leathery skin, and a good smile.

He closed his eyes and announced, "Dog? I don't

see no dog in here, sir." He winked like a burlesque comedian and touched one finger to his head in salute. "My name is Jeff," he said. "If you want anything—" And then he was gone.

"You see?" said Barbara. "And besides, you save fifty dollars, and coming back and another fifty, makes a hundred."

I am sure that Little Bit understood every word of the conversation. She stood up on the blotter and tilted her head, listening to Barbara, who said to her, "You know, Little Bit, you're not supposed to be on this ship at all. You mustn't let anybody see you. Now you hide, while we go down to eat."

There was a knock at the door. Silently Little Bit jumped to the floor and was out of sight.

It was the steward. He brought a little raw meat mixed with string beans on a plate covered with another plate. "Yes, sir," was all he said.

Barbara was asleep when the first rapport between me and Little Bit took place. I was sitting on a couch, reading, when she came into my cabin. By some magic trick, like an elevator going up a building shaft, she rose and seated herself next to me. She kept a hand's width of distance, tilted her head, and then lifted her lip over the left side of her face. I think I smiled back at her in the same fashion. I looked at her with interest for the first time—she was embarrassed. She looked away and then suddenly changed position, stretching her front legs ahead and sitting down flat on her hindlegs. She made several jerky movements but never uttered a sound.

Barbara's sleepy voice came from the other room. "Aren't you glad we have Little Bit with us?"

"Yes," I said, "I am." I thought about the miracles of nature, how this tough little lion in sheep's pelt functioned as she did; with a brain that could be no larger than an olive, she had memory, understanding, tact, courage, and no doubt loyalty, and she was completely self-sufficient. She smiled once more, and I smiled back: the relationship was established. Life went on as steadily as the ship.

On the afternoon of the third day out, as I lay in my deck chair reading, Barbara came running. "Little Bit is gone," she stammered with trembling lower lip.

We went down to the cabin. The steward was on all fours, looking under the beds and furniture. "Somebody musta left the door open," he said, "or it wasn't closed properly and swung open, and I suppose she got lonesome here all by herself and went looking for you. You should have taken her up to the movies with you, Miss."

"She's a smart dog," said Barbara. "Let's go to every spot on board where she might look for us."

So we went to the dining room, to the smoking room, the theater, the swimming pool, up the stairs, down the stairs, up on all the decks and around them, and to a secret little deck we had discovered between second and third class at the back of the ship, where Little Bit was taken for her exercise mornings and evenings and could run about freely while I stood guard.

A liner is as big as a city. She was nowhere.

When we got back the steward said, "I know where she is. You see, anybody finds a dog naturally takes it up to the kennels, and that's where she is. And there she stays for the rest of the trip. Remember, I never saw the dog, I don't know anything about her. The butcher—that's the man in charge of the kennels— he's liable to report me if he finds out I helped hide her. He's mean, especially about money. He figures that each passenger gives him ten bucks for taking care of a dog, and he doesn't want any of us to snatch it. There was a Yorkshire stowing away trip before last; he caught him at the gangplank as the dog was leaving the ship—the passenger had put him on a leash. Well, the butcher stopped him from getting off. He held up everything for hours, the man had to pay passage for the dog, and the steward who had helped hide him was fired. Herman Haegeli is his name, and he's as mean as they come. You'll find him on the top deck, near the aft chimney, where it says 'Kennels.' "

At such moments I enjoy the full confidence and affection of my child. Her nervous little hand is in mine, she willingly takes direction, her whole being is devotion, and no trouble is too much. She loved me especially then, because she knows that I am larcenous at heart and willing to go to the greatest lengths to beat a game and especially a meany.

"Now remember," I said, "if you want that dog back we have to be very careful. Let's first go and case the joint."

We climbed up into the scene of white and red ventilators, the sounds of humming wires, and the swish of the water. In yellow and crimson fire, the ball of the sun had half sunk into the sea, precisely at the end of the avenue of foam that the ship had plowed through the ocean. We were alone. We walked up and down, like people taking exercise before dinner, and the sea changed to violet and to indigo and then to that glossy gunmetal hue that it wears on moonless nights. The ship swished along to the even pulse of her machinery.

There was the sign. A yellow light shown from a porthole. I lifted Barbara, and inside, in one of the upper cages, was Little Bit, behind bars. There was no lock on her cage.

No one was inside. The door was fastened by a padlock. We walked back and forth for a while, and then a man came up the stairs, carrying a pail. He wore a gray cap, a towel around his neck, and a white coat such as butchers work in.

"That's our man," I said to Barbara.

Inside the kennels he brought forth a large dish that was like the body of a kettledrum. The dogs were barking.

"Now listen carefully, Barbara. I will go in and start a conversation with Mr. Haegeli. I will try to arrange it so that he turns his back on Little Bit's cage. At that moment, carefully open the door of the cage, grab Little Bit, put her under your coat, and then don't run—stand still, and after a while say, 'Oh, please let's get out of here.' I will then say good evening, and we both will leave very slowly. Remember to act calmly, watch the butcher, but don't expect a signal from me. Decide yourself when it is time to act. It might be when he is in the middle of work, or while he is talking."

"Oh, please, Poppy, let's get out of here," Barbara rehearsed.

I opened the door to the kennel and smiled like a tourist in appreciation of a new discovery. "Oh, that's where the dogs are kept," I said. "Good evening."

Mr. Haegeli answered with a grunt. He was mixing dog food.

"My, what nice food you're preparing for them. How much do they charge to take a dog across?"

"Fifty dollars," said Mr. Haegeli in a Swiss accent. There are all kinds of Swiss, some with French, some with Italian, and some with German accents. They all talk in a singing fashion. The faces are as varied as the accents. The butcher didn't look like a butcher—a good butcher is fat and rosy. Mr. Haegeli was thin-lipped, thin-nosed, his chin was pointed. In the light he didn't look as mean as I expected; he looked rather fanatic, and frustrated.

"How often do you feed them?"

"They eat twice a day and as good as anybody on board," said Mr. Haegeli. "All except Rolfi there— he belongs to an actor, Mr. Kruger, who crosses twice a year and brings the dog's food along." He pointed and Mr. Haegeli turned his back on Little Bit's cage to open Rolfi's. The entire place was immediately deafened with barking from a dozen cages. The breathless moment had arrived. Barbara was approaching the door, but the dog-lover Kruger spotted Little Bit and said, "There's a new one." He spoke to Little Bit, and Little Bit, who had behaved as if she had been carefully rehearsed for her liberation, turned away with tears in her eyes.

Mr. Kruger and his dog disappeared.

Mr. Haegeli wiped his hand on his apron and went back to mixing the dog food. The chances for rescuing Little Bit were getting slim.

"Where do you come from, Mr. Haegeli?"

"Schaffhausen. You know Schaffhausen?"

"Yes, yes," I said in German. *"Wunderbar."*

"Ja, ja, beautiful city."

"And the waterfall!"

"You know the Haegeli Wurstfabrik there?"

"No, I'm sorry."

"Well, it's one of the biggest sausage factories in Switzerland—liverwurst, salami, cervelat, frankfurters, boned hams—a big concern, belongs to a branch of my family. I'm sort of a wanderer. I like to travel—restless, you know—I can't see myself in Schaffhausen." He looked up. He was mixing food with both hands,

Kurt Kruger, the actor, said good evening and introduced himself. He spoke to Mr. Haegeli in German—and Mr. Haegeli turned his back on Little Bit's cage to open Rolfi's. The entire place was immediately deafened with barking from a dozen cages. The breathless moment had arrived. Barbara was approaching the door, but the dog-lover Kruger spotted Little Bit and said, "There's a new one." He spoke to Little Bit, and Little Bit, who had behaved as if she had been carefully rehearsed for her liberation, turned away with tears in her eyes.

Mr. Kruger and his dog disappeared.

Mr. Haegeli wiped his hand on his apron and went back to mixing the dog food. The chances for rescuing Little Bit were getting slim.

"Where do you come from, Mr. Haegeli?"

"Schaffhausen. You know Schaffhausen?"

"Yes, yes," I said in German. *"Wunderbar."*

"Ja, ja, beautiful city."

"And the waterfall!"

"You know the Haegeli Wurstfabrik there?"

"No, I'm sorry."

"Well, it's one of the biggest sausage factories in Switzerland—liverwurst, salami, cervelat, frankfurters, boned hams—a big concern, belongs to a branch of my family. I'm sort of a wanderer. I like to travel—restless, you know—I can't see myself in Schaffhausen." He looked up. He was mixing food with both hands, his arms rotating like an oversized eggbeater.

"I understand."

"Besides, we don't get along, my relatives and I. All they think about is money, small money—I think in large sums. I like a wide horizon. Schaffhausen is not for me."

"How long have you been traveling?"

"Oh, I've been two years on this ship. You see, I'm not really a butcher but an inventor."

"How interesting! What are you working on?"

At last Mr. Haegeli turned his back on the cage in which Little Bit waited. "Well, it's something tremendous. It's, so to say, revolutionary."

"Oh?"

"There's a friend of mine, a Swiss, who is a baker, but you know, like I'm not a real butcher, he is not exactly a baker—I mean, he knows his trade but he has ambition to make something of himself—and together we have created something that we call a frankroll." He waited for the effect.

"What is a frankroll?"

"It's a frankfurter baked inside a roll. We've got everything here to experiment with, the material and the ovens. I make the franks and he makes the rolls. We've tried it out on the passengers. Mr. Kruger, for example, says it's a marvelous idea. I might add that the experimental stage is over. Our product is perfect. Now it is a question of selling the patent, or licensing somebody—you know the way that is done. You make much more that way."

"Have you tried?"

Mr. Haegeli came close, the inventor's excitement in his eyes now. "That is where the hitch comes in. On the last trip I saw the biggest frankfurter people in America—they're in New York. Well, the things you find out! They were very nice. The president received us and looked at the product and tasted it. He liked it, because he called for his son and a man who works close to him. 'I think you've got something here,' said the old man. I think with him we would have had clear sailing, but he had one of these wisenheimers for a son."

As Haegeli talked he forgot completely about the dogs. He gesticulated with hands that were sticky with hash, using them as a boxer does when he talks with his gloves on. Standing close to me, he held them away lest dog food soil my clothes. He stood exactly right, with his back turned to the spot where Barbara was slowly reaching to the door of Little Bit's cage. It was all foiled again by the return of Mr. Kruger and Rolfi. Mr. Kruger kissed his dog good night and stood waiting while Rolfi slowly walked into his cage. He said to Rolfi that it was only for two more nights that he had to be here, he wished us a good night also, and after a final good night to his dog he went.

"Where was I?" said the butcher.

"With the frankroll, the old man, and the wise-guy son."

"Right. Well, the son was looking at our product with a mixture of doubt, so he took a bite out of it, and in the middle of it he stopped chewing. 'Mmmm,' he said. 'Not bad, not bad at all. But—' He paused a long time, and then he said, 'What about the mustard, gentlemen?'

"I said, 'All right, what about the mustard?'

"So the wise guy says, 'I'm a customer. I'm buying.

I'm at a hotdog stand. I watch the man in the white jacket. He picks up the frankfurter roll that's been sliced and placed face down on the hot plate—he picks it up in a sanitary fashion—and he takes the skinless frank with his prong and puts it in the roll and hands it to me. Now, I dip into the mustard pot, or maybe I decide on a little kraut, or maybe I want some condiments or relish. Anyway, I put that on the frank—' He held out his hand.

"So I said, 'What's all that got to do with our frankroll?'

"So Junior says, 'A lot. Let me explain. It's got no appeal. Practical maybe, but to put the mustard on the hot dog the customer would have to slice the frankfurter bun first, and that leads us straight back to the old-fashioned frankfurter and the old-fashioned roll. The frankroll may be practical, but it's got no sizzle to it. No eye appeal, no nose appeal—it's no good.'

"Well, the old man was confused, and he got up and said that he'd like to think about it, and then he said he'd like to show us the factory. Well, you'd never think how important a thing a frankfurter is. There are two schools of thought about frankfurters, the skin frank and the skinless. These people specialize in skinless ones—because the American housewife prefers them without the skin—but did you know that the skinless come with skins and have to be peeled? This factory is spotless. There is a vast hall, and at long tables sit hundreds of women, and music plays, and they all have in their left hand a frankfurter, and in the right a paring knife, and all day long they remove the skins from the frankfurters—an eight-hour day. And at the end of the room is a first-aid station, because at the speed at which they work there is a great deal of laceration. The man in charge—"

"Oh, please, Poppy, let's get out of here!" Barbara broke in.

"The man in charge explained that in spite of elaborate safety precautions there was a great deal of absenteeism on account of carelessness. They had people who were working on a machine to skin the frankfurters. 'Now if you could invent a frankfurter-skinning device,' said the old man to me, 'you'd be a millionaire overnight.' Well, we're not licked yet. The beauty of working on a ship is that you have everything on board. One of the engineers is working with us on a skinning machine, and I have another outfit lined up for the frankroll."

The light in Mr. Haegeli's eyes faded. He wiped his hand again on his apron, and I shook it, and slowly we walked out on deck and down the first flight of stairs to A deck. I said to Barbara, "Run for your life, for by now he has discovered that Little Bit is gone."

We got to the cabin. Little Bit smiled on both sides of her face, and she bounced from floor to chair to dresser. There was a knock on the door—the thrill of the game of cops and robbers had begun. Little Bit vanished.

Barbara asked innocently, "Who is it?"

It was the steward. "Did you find her?"

Barbara smiled.

"You got her back?"

Barbara nodded.

"Well, for heaven's sake, keep her out of sight. That crazy butcher is capable of anything—and I got a wife and family."

"From now on the dog must not be left," I said to Barbara. "She must go with us wherever we go, to the dining room, on deck to the lounge, and to the movies. And you can't carry her in that bag—you have to cover her with a scarf or have her inside your coat."

Barbara started going about as if she carried her arm in a sling. The steward averted his eyes whenever he met us, and he didn't bring any more dog food.

Mr. Kruger said, "The kennel man suspects you of having removed the dog from the kennel."

"We did."

"Good," said the actor. "Anything I can do, I will."

"Well, act as if you didn't know anything about it. How is Rolfi?"

"Oh, Rolfi is fine. You know, he's never bitten anybody in his life except that kennel man."

Mr. Kruger offered to get Little Bit off the boat. He had a wicker basket in which he carried some of Rolfi's things, and he would empty that, except for Rolfi's coat, and in that he would carry Little Bit off the *America,* for the butcher would follow us and watch us closely, and if he didn't find the dog before, he'd catch us at the customs.

"Isn't he a nice man—Mr. Kruger? People always

say such mean things about movie actors," said Barbara.

Camouflaged in a scarf, Little Bit rested on Barbara's lap during meals. On the deck chair she lay motionless between my feet, covered by a steamer rug. She traveled about under Barbara's coat, and she took her exercise on the secret afterdeck, while I watched from above.

After the morning walk, the next day, the steward knocked. He looked worried. "The butcher was here," he said, "and went all over the room. He found the dish with those French words and the dog's picture on it, on the bathroom floor."

"How could we be so careless?" I said, my professional pride hurt.

"And of course he saw the bag with *Little Bit* printed on it. I said I didn't know nothing about any dog."

We doubled our precautions. Little Bit's mouth was down at the edges with worry. I contemplated what to do. After all, there were only two more days, and if the worst happened we could sit upstairs with Little Bit, the way Mr. Kruger sat with Rolfi. I said to Barbara, "Perhaps it would be best to pay the passage and have it over with."

The symptoms were back. "No, you can't do that. Think of the poor steward and his family!"

"Well, we could settle that, I think, with the butcher. I don't like to cheat the line—"

"Well, Poppy, you can send them a check afterward, if that worries you, or drink a few extra bottles of champagne, or buy something in the shop."

Knock on the door.

"Who is it?"

"The purser, sir."

"Please come in."

The door opened. Behind the purser stood Mr. Haegeli.

"Just wanted to look and see if everything is all right. Are you comfortable, sir?"

"Everything is fine."

"By the way, sir, we're looking for a small white dog that's been lost. We wondered if by any chance it's in here."

"Come in and look for yourself."

"That's quite all right, sir. Excuse the intrusion. Good evening." The purser closed the door.

"What a nice man!" said Barbara.

The butcher was excluded from pursuing us in the public rooms of the ship; he couldn't follow us to the movies or the dining room. But he seemed to have spies. "What a lovely scarf you have there, Miss," said the elevator boy, and after that we used the stairs. The butcher came on deck in a fatigue uniform and followed us on the evening promenade around deck, during which Little Bit sat inside my overcoat, held in place by my right hand in a Napoleonic pose. We made four turns around the deck. I leaned against the railing once, holding Little Bit in place, so that I could stretch my arms; Barbara was skipping rope, and the maneuver fooled him. He ran downstairs, and we caught him as he emerged from near our cabin—he had made another search. We saw his shadow on the wall near the stairs several times. He seemed to be nearing a nervous breakdown. Mr. Kruger told us that he had sworn we had the dog and meant to find it at any cost. There was one more night to go, and the next day the ship would dock.

At ten Barbara would deliver Little Bit to Mr. Kruger, and we would fill the bag in which she traveled with paper tissue, tobacco, soap, extra toothbrushes, razorblades, dental floss, and other things, which can all be bought in Europe but which for some droll reason one always takes along.

Little Bit was fed from luncheon trays which we ordered for ourselves in the cabin instead of going down to lunch.

The steward was shaking. "I don't know," he said, "when that guy butchers, or when he takes care of the other dogs. He's hanging around here all the time. I hope you get off all right."

On the last afternoon on board I became careless. Some passengers and a bearded ship's officer were watching the last game of the deck-tennis tournament, and others were lying this way and that in their deck chairs, forming a protective barricade. Barbara had checked on the butcher—he was busy aft, airing some of his charges.

I thought it safe to take Little Bit out of my coat and place her on deck, so that we all could relax a bit. She had been there but a moment when I heard a cry.

"Ha," it went. It was the "Ha" of accusation and discovery, chagrin and triumph, and it had been issued by
Mr. Haegeli, who stood with both arms raised. Fortunately he was not a kangaroo and was therefore unable to jump over the occupied deck chairs. I gathered
up Little Bit, and we were safe for a few seconds. By
now I knew the ship's plan as well as the man who de-
signed her. We went down two decks on outside stairs,
entered through a serving pantry, climbed one inside
service stair, and then nonchalantly walked to the bar.
I sat down and rang for the steward. I ordered something to drink. In a little while Barbara, with her lem-
onade in hand, said, "He's watching us through the
third window!"

I swept my eyes over the left side of the room, and
his face was pressed against the glass, pale and haunt-
ing. He kept watch from the outside, and ran back and
forth as we moved around inside.

We went down to dinner. When we came back I
got a cigar. He was outside the bar. As I went to the
saloon to have coffee he was outside that window.

"Don't give Little Bit any sugar," Barbara said.
"He's watching us every minute."

The floor was cleared for dancing, and we got up
to walk back to the library. There is a passage between
the main saloon and the library off which are various
pantries and side rooms, and it has no window. In a
corner of it is the shop, and on this last evening people
stood there in numbers buying cartons of cigarettes,
film, small sailor hats, miniature lifebelts and ship

models with "*S.S. America*" written on them. Here I suddenly realized the miraculous solution of our problem. It was in front of me, on a shelf. Among stuffed Mickey Mice, Donald Ducks, and teddy bears of various sizes stood the exact replica of Little Bit—the same button eyes and patent-leather nose, the fluff, the legs like sticks, the pompom at the end of the tail, and the blue ribbon in its hair.

"How much is that dog?" I asked the young lady.

"Two ninety-five."

"I'll take it."

"Shall I wrap it up, sir?"

"No, thanks, I'll take it as is."

"What are we going to do now, Poppy?"

"Now you keep Little Bit hidden, and I'll take the stuffed dog, and we'll go into the library."

There we sat down. I placed the stuffed dog at my side and spoke to it. The butcher was on the far side of the ship, but he almost went through the window. He disappeared and ran around to the other side. I had arranged the toy dog so that it seemed to be asleep at my side, partly covered by Barbara's scarf. I told her to take Little Bit down to the cabin and then come back, and we'd have some fun with the butcher.

When she came back Barbara took the toy dog and fixed its hair and combed the fluff. Then I said, "Please give me the dog." We walked the length of the ship on the inside. The butcher was sprinting outside, his face flashing momentarily in the series of windows.

At the front of the ship we went out on deck. I held

the dog so that the pompom stuck out in back, and I wiggled it a little, to give it the illusion of life. It took the butcher a while to catch up. He walked fast—we walked faster. He almost ran—we ran. He shouted, "Mister!" I continued running. As we came toward the stern I asked Barbara, "Can you let out a terrible scream?"

"Yes, of course," said Barbara.

"One—two—three—*now*."

She screamed, and I threw the dog in a wide curve out into the sea. The butcher, a few feet away, gripped the railing and looked below, where the small white form was bobbing up and down in the turbulent water. Rapidly it was washed away in the wake of the *America*.

We turned to go back into the saloon.

We left the butcher paralyzed at the stern. He wasn't at the gangplank the next day.

Little Bit landed in France without further incident.

Why did

THE BETTING
SCOTCHMAN

ANONYMOUS   *throw away £100?*

THE COLONEL of the Red Hussars was an Irishman, who was as proud of his nationality as it is possible for an Irishman to be, and that is not saying a little by any means. He carried his patriotism so far as to aver that not only were the Irish the finest, the most courageous, the most gifted, of the four nationalities, but that nearly all the great Englishmen were really Irishmen. He justified this Hibernianism by a mode of reasoning that was highly original, but not wholly convincing. It would have provoked shouts of laughter in the mess if it had proceeded from the lips of a subaltern, but the colonel was an altogether different person to deal with. It would be dangerous to quarrel with him, and he was as peppery as an old maid who has been jilted by the curate. It was considered far more advisable to give him his way and to let him exhaust himself by the violence of his own efforts.

When he launched out on his favorite topic, therefore, he was listened to in disrespectful silence by his subordinates; but in revenge it was the greatest delight of the wags of the regiment to mimic his voice and manner, and to represent him as uttering the most astounding Hibernian falsehoods, garnished with numerous expressions of a wholly unprintable character. This was a very popular amusement in every messroom where the colonel's personality was known. His name, as the army list will tell you, was Colonel Dominick Sydney Power, but this is a trifling detail. He had been nicknamed Old Pat at a very early stage of his military career.

Therefore, when the Red Hussars heard that Sir James Macleod had been gazetted from the Blues to their own regiment, conjecture ran very rife among the officers whether Sir James would contrive to hit it off amicably with Old Pat. It was generally felt that the stranger would probably prove a Scotchman of the deepest dye, with a very large allotment of Scotch pride and patriotism. No doubt, after his experiences in the Blues, he would be inclined to regard a mere colonel in a hussar regiment with more compassion than reverence. Under these circumstances, there seemed to be every prospect of some lively scenes when the colonel should deem it fitting to take the Scotch baronet into his confidence on the important subject of national distinctions.

"It will be great fun if he goes for Old Pat, and gives it to him when he begins the usual rot," said young Fanshawe, with a broad grin, and it was generally agreed among the junior officers of the regiment that it would be great fun indeed.

While his subordinates were coming to this insubordinate decision, Colonel Dominick Power was engaged in reading a long letter from an old schoolfellow of his, and a former brother-officer of Sir James Macleod's to whom he had written in order to make some inquiries with regard to the new importation into the mess-room of the Red Hussars, and the baronet's motives for effecting the exchange.

"A woman is at the bottom of it, as usual," wrote Captain Fletcher, of the Blues. "Macleod was very hard hit, and she threw him over for no reason that any one can divine. Pure deviltry, that is all. He knew that you were ordered abroad, and he wants to get out of the country without appearing to run away. That's the story. He is a capital fellow; no nonsense about him in any way; is a good sportsman; A-one shot; and very popular in the regiment. There is only one point on which I had better caution you. *Don't bet with him.* He is a very devil at bets, and always wins."

"Is he, indeed?" mused Colonel Power; "and he may be the very divil himself for all he'll get out of me. It's meself that would like to see the colonel of the regiment betting with a mere whipper-snapper of a subaltern!"

Sir James Macleod proved to be a tall, fair young man, whose long features and high cheek-bones testified very clearly that the place of his birth lay beyond the Tweed. He was not remarkably good-looking, but he carried himself with such an air of distinction that it seemed wonderful, as young Fanshawe said, that any woman could throw over "such a dasher, and a real, live baronet to boot." His manner, however, was that of a man of the world; and it is not remarkable, under the circumstances, that he got on at once with the young men who were to be his companions for the future.

"We thought you would be no end of a heavy swell," said young Fanshawe, in a day or two, during which friendship had ripened into familiarity; "but you ain't a bit."

Whereat Sir James Macleod laughed good-humoredly.

"What shall you do when Old Pat begins his usual rot," continued Fanshawe, in a confidential tone, "about Ireland being the finest country in the universe, and everybody else being miserable scarecrows and outsiders? Shall you stick up for Auld Reekie? I wish you would. It would make Pat so sick!"

Young Fanshawe explained his meaning at some length.

"And you think that he would be furious if any one contradicted him?" inquired Macleod, fixing a very wary grey eye on the other.

"Furious! He would have a fit."

Macleod deliberated for a moment with the same wary expression of eye, and then he said quietly:

"I should like to make a bet with you. I will lay you two guineas to a five-pound note that, if you will draw the colonel out on his favorite topic, I will contradict him on every point, we will have a most angry discussion, and at the end the colonel will be as good-humored and pleased as if—well, as if I had put a hundred pounds in his pocket."

"You don't know Old Pat," replied Fanshawe, shaking his head. "He'll make the regiment too hot to hold you in less than no time."

"Well, shall I book the bet?" suggested Macleod blandly.

"No; I won't bet on a certainty."

"*Are* you sure," inquired Macleod, with an air of doubt, "that it isn't that you don't feel . . . quite . . . up . . . to drawing Old Pat——"

"You may book the bet," cried Fanshawe haughtily, and his cheek flushed with anger. "And if you lose, you will have no one to thank but yourself."

"Quite so," said Macleod calmly, and he made the entry in his pocketbook in the most businesslike way. "And if I lose—well, at any rate I shall afford you some amusement."

And so it came about that that same evening, after dinner, when the wine was circulating pretty freely, and a mellow glow was beginning to make its appearance on the colonel's ripe visage, young Fanshawe, to the consternation of the mess, introduced the subject of a deceased Irish politician.

"What a scoundrel that fellow was!" said young Fanshawe, apropos of nothing.

The other subs looked at young Fanshawe with an expression of amazement. Had he gone out of his senses, or had the wine got into his head? Closer inspection, however, showed that he looked unnaturally sober and unusually intelligent. Then there must be some game on—some game at the colonel's expense. This would probably be good sport, and it would be well to be in at the death. Every eye was fixed on the colonel. Old Pat was not to be drawn by young Fanshawe. He snorted indignantly, but reserved his steel for worthier foes.

The circle of watchful eyes now turned to Fanshawe. What would be his next move?

"My *pater* has just bought a hogshead of the finest Scotch whisky," said the youth, coming up to time with commendable alacrity and a cheerful smile. He launched out into some details on the subject, concluding with the following significant remark:

"I hate Irish whisky. It is such sickening, soapy stuff. I think Scotch is much the best."

A joyful gleam shone in the attentive optics. This was getting interesting. Young Fanshawe was actually, of malice prepense, going for Old Pat.

"Hooray! Yoicks! Tallyho! Go it, young Fanshawe!" were the sentiments reflected in the breasts of that hopeful youth's brother-subalterns; while even the major, who certainly ought to have known better, grinned with intense enjoyment.

"Don't you think so, Macleod?" said young Fanshawe to the Scotchman, who was cracking walnuts
with the utmost insouciance.

"Don't I think what?" he replied.

"That Scotch whisky is better than Irish."

"Why, of course. Can there be any doubt? Does
any one dispute it?"

This sally was too much for Old Pat. He plunged
at once into the fray, and a heated discussion ensued.
At least, it was heated on his side, for Macleod retained
an appearance of judicial calm that would have put Job
himself in a bad temper. Young Fanshawe, it may be
added, at once seized the opportunity to retire from
the forefront of the battle, and took up the safe position of an interested spectator.

In a comparatively short time a great deal of un-
palatable information was shot upon the colonel. He
was told that not only was Scotch whisky far more
pleasing to the taste than Irish, but it was less injurious
to the health, and there was less of illicit distillation in
Scotland than in Ireland. Warming apparently to his
subject, and totally regardless of Old Pat's passionate
and profane defense, Macleod went on to enunciate
the view that all that was really good and great in the
Irish nation was English or Scotch in origin, that the
Irish colonies in English towns formed the most criminal and degraded portion of the population, and that
there was actually something in the climate or the soil
of Ireland which deteriorated the physical and moral

nature of the inhabitants.

He said this with the calm utterance of a lecturer who demonstrates facts. There was even a softer undertone perceptible now and then, as if he pitied the advocate of so miserable a cause.

The colonel became almost incoherent with rage. His face assumed a deep purple hue. He manifested an inclination to foam at the mouth.

"For proof of this," continued Macleod, "it is quite enough to refer to a well-known and incontrovertible fact. Whether it is due to the potatoes that they eat or the bog-water that they drink, I don't know; but everyone knows that every Irishman of anything like ancient descent has a black roof to his mouth. You will bear me out in that, colonel, I am sure."

The mess in vain endeavored to preserve a dignified demeanor. They were nearly choking with suppressed laughter. Young Fanshawe contrived to upset a decanter in order to hide his emotion. Another young scapegrace was obliged to go to the sideboard, where he gurgled subterraneously for several minutes with his back to the company.

"It's a lie!" roared the colonel, whose eyes were nearly starting out of his head. "An infernal lie!"

"How? A lie, colonel? Do you mean to deny what I have stated?"

"I mean," shrieked Old Pat, "that the Powers of Ballycoran are one of the oldest families in Irreland; that they were on intimate terms with Brian Boru; and that whin the blissid St. Patrick came that way, 'twas me own ancestorr that gave him the *cead mille failthe* to Ballycoran; and if ye can find a single black roof in the mouths of the entirre family, may the divil fly off with the soul of the dirty varmin!"

And with these words the colonel struck the table a blow that made the glasses ring.

"This is very interesting, indeed," replied Macleod, gazing at the colonel as if that dignitary were the missing link, or a new form of butterfly. "I had no idea that any one—even an Irishman—would dispute it. Now, I dare say that you have never thought of examining your own mouth?"

The colonel's reply was of a nature that would have been an expensive one had he made it in the presence of a magistrate who enforced the penalties against swearing.

"Strange, very strange," said Macleod, who was still quite calm. "Now, I think I will lay you two to one in ten-pound notes that I am right."

A wolfish light shone in the colonel's eyes, but he held back with the most praiseworthy self-control. It would undignified to bet with a mere sub—and on such a subject.

"I will make it five to one in twenty-pound notes," continued Macleod, with an air of great confidence, "that you have a black roof to your mouth."

"I will take that bet," spluttered the colonel, who was now in a white heat of rage. "By me soul, I will take that same, just to teach you not to bet on subjects of which you know nothing. It will be a useful lesson.

And now, how do you propose to decide the bet?"

Sir James Macleod suggested that ocular inspection would be the quickest and most satisfactory method—ocular inspection by the senior officers of the mess. Their words would probably be sufficient for both parties.

The colonel demurred a little to his proposition. It seemed to him totally subversive of discipline. He was quite sure that the commander-in-chief would not approve of it. No other possible way of settling the question occurred to him, however, and, now that he had got so far, he was determined to win that hundred pounds at all hazards, and give the young Scotch jackanapes his much-needed lesson.

Candles were accordingly sent for at once, and a dead silence ensued. Every man looked at the other as if inquiring what would be the next act in this singular drama. Even young Fanshawe forgot to laugh. The colonel breathed heavily, and his eyes glared at his adversary, who still retained his unmoved demeanor.

At last the lights came. Armed each with a candlestick, the major, the captains, and the senior subaltern in turn examined the gaping orifice which the colonel revealed to their gaze, during which inspection young Fanshawe threw himself headlong on to a sofa and kicked like a person in mortal agony; while two subalterns expressed their feelings in a bear-fight behind the colonel's unconscious head.

The verdict of the judges was unanimous. They declared that the roof of the colonel's mouth was red, not black.

"Decidedly red," said the senior captain, with a curious chuckle that seemed fraught with a world of meaning. "Not a trace of black."

"Not black?" cried Sir James Macleod in tones of amazement. "Are you sure?"

"Quite sure," replied the major judicially.

"'Pon honor!" remarked the others in chorus.

"Well, gentlemen, you *have* surprised me," said Macleod, glancing from one to the other, as if he could scarcely believe his ears. "Of course I believe you, but—if the colonel will permit—I should like to look just to convince my own eyes."

"Look away, me boy," chuckled the colonel hoarsely. He was convulsed with delight at his complete triumph. "Ye'll have to pay for your peep!"

"Well, then, please open your mouth a little wider, colonel; and will one of you hold the light? Really, colonel, you must excuse me, but I can't see. You must really let me open your mouth a little wider."

With these words he actually laid one sacrilegious hand on the colonel's nose and the other on the colonel's chin, and pressed them gently in opposite directions. There was not a man among all the reckless crew that stood around but held his breath in anticipation of a terrible explosion.

The colonel did not rise and annihilate the audacious Scotchman. He bore this insult like a lamb. The indignity was, however, of the very shortest duration, for Macleod was satisfied with the briefest glance.

"I have lost," he said quite cheerfully. "And I owe you an apology, colonel. Luckily, I have the notes about me."

He produced his pocketbook, extracted two fifty-pound notes from it, and handed them to the colonel. The latter took them with the most portentous gravity. He was clearly puzzled and uncertain as to the right course of action. He puckered up his face in the most curious wrinkles. Then he rubbed his nose reflectively. The humorous side of the question, however, presented itself very forcibly to him, and he broke into a broad grin.

"Well," he said, with a loud roar of laughter, "you are an impudent rascal! But I didn't think that a Scotchman and his money were so easily parted."

And amid sympathetic roars from the entire mess, who thought the whole thing a capital joke all around, the colonel's indignation melted into intense enjoyment of his own success. The only person who was unsettled in his mind was young Fanshawe, who could not understand why Macleod should have risked a hundred pounds in so foolish a way.

"I don't think much of that Scotch chap you sent us," wrote the colonel, a few days later, to his old schoolfellow, Captain Fletcher, of the Blues. "Too much brag; too little bottom. He'll never set the Thames on fire. Only a few nights ago he actually bet me a hundred pounds to twenty that I had a black roof to my mouth—cheeky young devil! Well, I took the bet, just to give him a lesson. You ought to have seen his face when he lost. Really, I couldn't help roaring with laughter to see how confident he had been and how sold he was. You must be a dull lot in the Blues if he always wins from you. Anyhow, I have broken the record."

Captain Fletcher wrote by return of post to his old schoolfellow, Colonel Dominick Power:

"Confound you! Didn't I caution you most point-edly not to bet with him? Couldn't you have known that there must be some deviltry on, or a man would not throw away his money in such preposterous fashion?

"Before he left us, Macleod laid me one hundred pounds to a thousand that he would pull your nose in the presence of the mess before he had been a week in the regiment, and without being courtmartialed or even placed under arrest for it; and I have just received a round-robin letter signed by your mess, declaring that he has won the bet."

MAX SHULMAN (1919-   )

...is a genius at satire and an outrageous punster. This beloved American humorist wrote his first book, Barefoot Boy with Cheek, *at 24.*

Recently, his situation comedy The Adventures of Dobie Gillis, *about a teen-age hero, has been viewed on television by millions.*

His Broadway hit, The Tender Trap, *and a best selling novel,* Rally Round The Flag Boys!, *have kept his audience chuckling.*

LOVE IS A FALLACY

and logic but a snare

COOL WAS I and logical. Keen, calculating, perspicacious, acute, and astute—I was all of these. My brain was as powerful as a dynamo, as precise as a chemist's scales, as penetrating as a scalpel. And—think of it!—I was only eighteen.

It is not often that one so young has such a giant intellect. Take, for example, Petey Bellows, my roommate at the university. Same age, same background, but dumb as an ox. A nice enough fellow, you understand, but nothing upstairs. Emotional type. Unstable. Impressionable. Worst of all, a faddist. Fads, I submit, are the very negation of reason. To be swept up in every new craze that comes along, so surrender yourself to idiocy just because everybody else is doing it—this, to me, is the acme of mindlessness. Not, however, to Petey.

One afternoon I found Petey lying on his bed with an expression of such distress on his face that I immediately diagnosed appendicitis. "Don't move," I said. "Don't take a laxative. I'll get a doctor."

"Raccoon," he mumbled thickly.

"Raccoon?" I said, pausing in my flight.

"I want a raccoon coat," he wailed.

I perceived that his trouble was not physical, but mental. "Why do you want a raccoon coat?"

"I should have known it," he cried, pounding his temples. "I should have known they'd come back when the Charleston came back. Like a fool I spent all my money for textbooks, and now I can't get a raccoon coat."

"Can you mean," I said incredulously, "that people are actually wearing raccoon coats again?"

"All the Big Men on Campus are wearing them. Where've you been?"

"In the library," I said, naming a place not frequented by Big Men on Campus.

He leaped from the bed and paced the room. "I've got to have a raccoon coat," he said passionately. "I've got to!"

"Petey, why? Look at it rationally. Raccoon coats are unsanitary. They shed. They smell bad. They weigh too much. They're unsightly. They————"

"You don't understand," he interrupted impatiently. "It's the thing to do. Don't you want to be in the swim?"

"No," I said truthfully.

"Well, I do," he declared. "I'd give anything for a raccoon coat. Anything!"

My brain, that precision instrument, slipped into high gear. "Anything?" I asked, looking at him narrowly.

"Anything," he affirmed in ringing tones.

I stroked my chin thoughtfully. It so happened that I knew where to get my hands on a raccoon coat. My father had had one in his undergraduate days; it lay now in a trunk in the attic back home. It also happened that Petey had something I wanted. He didn't *have* it exactly, but at least he had first rights on it. I refer to his girl, Polly Espy.

I had long coveted Polly Espy. Let me emphasize that my desire for this young woman was not emotional in nature. She was, to be sure, a girl who excited the emotions, but I was not one to let my heart rule my head. I wanted Polly for a shrewdly calculated, entirely cerebral reason.

I was a freshman in law school. In a few years I would be out in practice. I was well aware of the importance of the right kind of wife in furthering a lawyer's career. The successful lawyers I had observed were, almost without exception, married to beautiful, gracious, intelligent women. With one omission, Polly fitted these specifications perfectly.

Beautiful she was. She was not yet of pin-up proportions, but I felt sure that time would supply the lack. She already had the makings.

Gracious she was. By gracious I mean full of graces. She had an erectness of carriage, an ease of bearing, a poise that clearly indicated the best of breeding. At table her manners were exquisite. I had seen her at the Kozy Kampus Korner eating the specialty of the house —a sandwich that contained scraps of pot roast, gravy, chopped nuts, and a dipper of sauerkraut—without even getting her fingers moist.

Intelligent she was not. In fact, she veered in the opposite direction. But I believed that under my guidance she would smarten up. At any rate, it was worth a try. It is, after all, easier to make a beautiful dumb girl smart than to make an ugly smart girl beautiful.

"Petey," I said, "are you in love with Polly Espy?"

"I think she's a keen kid," he replied, "but I don't know if you'd call it love. Why?"

"Do you," I asked, "have any kind of formal arrangement with her? I mean are you going steady or anything like that?"

"No. We see each other quite a bit, but we both have other dates. Why?"

"Is there," I asked, "any other man for whom she has a particular fondness?"

"Not that I know of. Why?"

I nodded with satisfaction. "In other words, if you were out of the picture, the field would be open. Is that right?"

"I guess so. What are you getting at?"

"Nothing, nothing," I said innocently, and took my suitcase out of the closet.

"Where you going?" asked Petey.

"Home for the week-end." I threw a few things into the bag.

"Listen," he said, clutching my arm eagerly, "while you're home, you couldn't get some money from your old man, could you, and lend it to me so I can buy a raccoon coat?"

"I may do better than that," I said with a mysterious wink and closed my bag and left.

"Look," I said to Petey when I got back Monday morning. I threw open the suitcase and revealed the huge, hairy, gamy object that my father had worn in his Stutz Bearcat in 1925.

"Holy Toledo!" said Petey reverently. He plunged his hands into the raccoon coat and then his face. "Holy Toledo!" he repeated fifteen or twenty times.

"Would you like it?" I asked.

"Oh, yes!" he cried, clutching the greasy pelt to him. Than a canny look came into his eyes. "What do you want for it?"

"Your girl," I said, mincing no words.

"Polly?" he said in a horrified whisper. "You want Polly?"

"That's right."

He flung the coat from him. "Never," he said stoutly.

I shrugged. "Okay. If you don't want to be in the swim, I guess it's your business."

I sat down in a chair and pretended to read a book, but out of the corner of my eye I kept watching Petey. He was a torn man. First he looked at the coat with the expression of a waif at a bakery window. Then he turned away and set his jaw resolutely. Then he looked back at the coat, with even more longing in his face. Then he turned away, but not so much resolution this time. Back and forth his head swiveled, desire waxing, resolution waning. Finally he didn't turn away at all; he just stood and stared with mad lust at the coat.

"It isn't as though I was in love with Polly," he said thickly. "Or going steady or anything like that."

"That's right," I murmured.

"What's Polly to me, or me to Polly?"

"Not a thing," said I.

"It's just been a casual kick—just a few laughs, that's all."

"Try on the coat," said I.

He complied. The coat bunched high over his ears and dropped all the way down to his shoe tops. He looked like a mound of dead raccoons. "Fits fine," he said happily.

I rose from my chair. "Is it a deal?" I asked, extending my hand.

He swallowed. "It's a deal," he said and shook my hand.

I had my first date with Polly the following evening. This was in the nature of a survey; I wanted to find out just how much work I had to do to get her mind up to the standard I required. I took her first to dinner. "Gee, that was a delish dinner," she said as we left the restaurant. Then I took her to a movie. "Gee, that was a marvy movie," she said as we left the theater. And then

I took her home. "Gee, I had a sensaysh time," she said as she bade me good night.

I went back to my room with a heavy heart. I had gravely underestimated the size of my task. This girl's lack of information was terrifying. Nor would it be enough merely to supply her with information. First she had to be taught to *think*. This loomed as a project of no small dimensions, and at first I was tempted to give her back to Petey. But then I got to thinking about her abundant physical charms and about the way she entered a room and the way she handled a knife and fork, and I decided to make an effort.

I went about it, as in all things, systematically. I gave her a course in logic. It happened that I, as a law student, was taking a course in logic myself, so I had the all the facts at my fingertips. "Polly," I said to her when I picked her up on our next date, "tonight we are going over to the Knoll and talk."

"Oo, terrif," she replied. One thing I will say for this girl: you would go far to find another so agreeable.

We went to the Knoll, the campus trysting place, and we sat down under an old oak, and she looked at me expectantly.

"What are we going to talk about?" she asked.

"Logic."

She thought this over for a minute and decided she liked it. "Magnif," she said.

"Logic," I said, clearing my throat, "is the science of thinking. Before we can think correctly, we must first learn to recognize the common fallacies of logic. These we will take up tonight."

"Wow-dow!" she cried, clapping her hands delightedly.

I winced but went bravely on. "First let us examine the fallacy called Dicto Simpliciter."

"By all means," she urged, batting her lashes eagerly.

"Dicto Simpliciter means an argument based on an unqualified generalization. For example: Exercise is good. Therefore everybody should exercise."

"I agree," said Polly earnestly. "I mean exercise is wonderful. I mean it builds the body and everything."

"Polly," I said gently, "the argument is a fallacy. *Exercise is good* is an unqualified generalization. For instance, if you have heart disease, exercise is bad, not good. Many people are ordered by their doctors *not* to exercise. You must *qualify* the generalization. You must say exercise is *usually* good, or exercise is good for *most people*. Otherwise you have committed a Dicto Simpliciter. Do you see?"

"No," she confessed. "But this is marvy. Do more! Do more!"

"It will be better if you stop tugging at my sleeve," I told her, and when she desisted, I continued. "Next we take up a fallacy called Hasty Generalization. Listen carefully: You can't speak French. I can't speak French. Petey Bellows can't speak French. I must therefore conclude that nobody at the University of Minnesota can speak French."

"Really?" said Polly, amazed. *"Nobody?"*

I hid my exasperation. "Polly, it's a fallacy. The generalization is reached too hastily. There are too few instances to support such a conclusion."

"Know any more fallacies?" she asked breathlessly. "This is more fun than dancing even."

I fought off a wave of despair. I was getting nowhere with this girl, absolutely nowhere. Still, I am nothing if not persistent. I continued. "Next comes Post Hoc. Listen to this: Let's not take Bill on our picnic. Every time we take him out with us, it rains."

"I know somebody just like that," she exclaimed. "A girl back home—Eula Becker, her name is. It never fails. Every single time we take her on a picnic——"

"Polly," I said sharply, "it's a fallacy. Eula Becker doesn't *cause* the rain. She has no connection with the rain. You are guilty of Post Hoc if you blame Eula Becker."

"I'll never do it again," she promised contritely. "Are you mad at me?"

I sighed. "No, Polly, I'm not mad."

"Then tell me some more fallacies.' '

"All right. Let's try Contradictory Premises."

"Yes, let's," she chirped, blinking her eyes happily.

I frowned, but went ahead. "Here's an example of Contradictory Premises. If God can do anything, can He make a stone so heavy that He won't be able to lift it?"

"Of course," she replied promptly.

"But if He can do anything, He can lift the stone," I pointed out.

"Yeah," she said thoughtfully. "Well, then, I guess

He can't make the stone."

"But He can do anything," I reminded her.

She scratched her pretty, empty head. "I'm all confused," she admitted.

"Of course you are. Because when the premises of an argument contradict each other, there can be no argument. If there is an irresistible force, there can be no immovable object. If there is an immovable object, there can be no irresistible force. Get it?"

"Tell me some more of this keen stuff," she said eagerly.

I consulted my watch. "I think we'd better call it a night. I'll take you home now, and you go over all the things you've learned. We'll have another session tomorrow night."

I deposited her at the girls' dormitory, where she assured me that she had had a perfectly terrif evening, and I went glumly home to my room. Petey lay snoring in his bed, the raccoon coat huddled like a great hairy beast at his feet. For a moment I considered waking him and telling him that he could have his girl back. It seemed clear that my project was doomed to failure. The girl simply had a logic-proof head.

But then I reconsidered. I had wasted one evening; I might as well waste another. Who knew? Maybe somewhere in the extinct crater of her mind a few embers still smoldered. Maybe somehow I could fan them into a flame. Admittedly it was not a prospect fraught with hope, but I decided to give it one more try.

Seated under the oak the next evening, I said, "Our

first fallacy tonight is called Ad Misericordiam."

She quivered with delight.

"Listen closely," I said. "A man applies for a job. When the boss asks him what his qualifications are, he replies that he has a wife and six children at home, the wife is a helpless cripple, the children have nothing to eat, no clothes to wear, no shoes on their feet, there are no beds in the house, no coal in the cellar, and winter is coming."

A tear rolled down each of Polly's pink cheeks. "Oh, this is awful, awful," she sobbed.

"Yes, it's awful," I agreed, "but it's no argument. The man never answered the boss's question about his qualifications. Instead he appealed to the boss's sympathy. He committed the fallacy of Ad Misericordiam. Do you understand?"

"Have you got a handkerchief?" she blubbered.

I handed her a handkerchief and tried to keep from screaming while she wiped her eyes. "Next," I said in a carefully controlled tone, "we will discuss False Analogy. Here is an example: Students should be allowed to look at their textbooks during examinations. After all, surgeons have X rays to guide them during an operation, lawyers have briefs to guide them during a trial, carpenters have blueprints to guide them when they are building a house. Why, then, shouldn't students be allowed to look at their textbooks during an examination?"

"There now," she said enthusiastically, "is the most marvy idea I've heard in years."

"Polly," I said testily, "the argument is all wrong. Doctors, lawyers, and carpenters aren't taking a test to see how much they have learned, but students are. The situations are altogether different, and you can't make an analogy between them."

"I still think it's a good idea," said Polly.

"Nuts," I muttered. Doggedly I pressed on. "Next we'll try Hypothesis Contrary to Fact."

"Sounds yummy," was Polly's reaction.

"Listen: If Madame Curie had not happened to leave a photographic plate in a drawer with a chunk of pitchblende, the world today would not know about radium."

"True, true," said Polly, nodding her head. "Did you see the movie? Oh, it just knocked me out. That Walter Pidgeon is so dreamy. I mean he fractures me."

"If you can forget Mr. Pidgeon for a moment," I said coldly, "I would like to point out that the statement is a fallacy. Maybe Madame Curie would have discovered radium at some later date. Maybe somebody else would have discovered it. Maybe any number of things would have happened. You can't start with a hypothesis that is not true and then draw any supportable conclusions from it."

"They ought to put Walter Pidgeon in more pictures," said Polly. "I hardly ever see him any more."

One more chance, I decided. But just one more. There is a limit to what flesh and blood can bear. "The next fallacy is called Poisoning the Well."

"How cute!" she gurgled.

"Two men are having a debate. The first one gets up and says, 'My opponent is a notorious liar. You can't believe a word that he is going to say.' Now, Polly, think. Think hard. What's wrong?"

I watched her closely as she knit her creamy brow in concentration. Suddenly a glimmer of intelligence—the first I had seen—came into her eyes. "It's not fair," she said with indignation. "It's not a bit fair. What chance has the second man got if the first man calls him a liar before he even begins talking?"

"Right!" I cried exultantly. "One hundred per cent right. It's not fair. The first man has *poisoned the well* before anybody could drink from it. He has hamstrung his opponent before he could even start. . . . Polly, I'm proud of you."

"Pshaw," she murmured, blushing with pleasure.

"You see, my dear, these things aren't so hard. All you have to do is concentrate. Thank — examine — evaluate. Come now, let's review everything we have learned."

"Fire away," she said with an airy wave of her hand.

Heartened by the knowledge that Polly was not altogether a cretin, I began a long, patient review of all I had told her. Over and over and over again I cited instances, pointed out flaws, kept hammering away without letup. It was like digging a tunnel. At first everything was work, sweat, and darkness. I had no idea when I would reach the light, or even *if* I would. But I persisted. I pounded and clawed and scraped, and finally I was rewarded. I saw a chink of light. And then the chink got bigger and the sun came pouring in and all was bright.

Five grueling nights this took, but it was worth it. I had made a logician out of Polly; I had taught her to think. My job was done. She was worthy of me at last. She was a fit wife for me, a proper hostess for my many mansions, a suitable mother for my well-heeled children.

It must not be thought that I was without love for this girl. Quite the contrary. Just as Pygmalion loved the perfect women he had fashioned, so I loved mine. I decided to acquaint her with my feelings at our very next meeting. The time had come to change our relationship from academic to romantic.

"Polly," I said when next we sat beneath our oak, "tonight we will not discuss fallacies."

"Aw, gee," she said, disappointed.

"My dear," I said, favoring her with a smile, "we have now spent five evenings together. We have gotten along splendidly. It is clear that we are well matched."

"Hasty Generalization," said Polly brightly.

"I beg your pardon," said I.

"Hasty Generalization," she repeated. "How can you say that we are well matched on the basis of only five dates?"

I chuckled with amusement. The dear child had learned her lessons well. "My dear," I said, patting her hand in a tolerant manner, "five dates is plenty. After all, you don't have to eat a whole cake to know that it's good."

"False Analogy," said Polly promptly. "I'm not a cake. I'm a girl."

I chuckled with somewhat less amusement. The dear child had learned her lessons perhaps too well. I decided to change tactics. Obviously the best approach was a simple, strong, direct declaration of love. I paused for a moment while my massive brain chose the proper words. Then I began:

"Polly, I love you. You are the whole world to me, and the moon and the stars and the constellations of outer space. Please, my darling, say that you will go steady with me, for if you will not, life will be meaningless. I will languish. I will refuse my meals. I will wander the earth, a shambling, hollow-eyed hulk."

There, I thought that ought to do it.

"Ad Misericordiam," said Polly.

I ground my teeth. I was not Pygmalion; I was Frankenstein, and my monster had me by the throat. Frantically I fought back the tide of panic surging through me. At all costs I had to keep cool.

"Well, Polly," I said, forcing a smile, "you certainly have learned your fallacies."

"You're darn right," she said with a vigorous nod.

"And who taught them to you, Polly?"

"You did."

"That's right. So you do owe me something, don't you, my dear? If I hadn't come along you never would have learned about fallacies."

"Hypothesis Contrary to Face," she said instantly.

I dashed perspiration from my brow. "Polly," I

croaked, "you mustn't take all these things so literally. I mean this is just classroom stuff. You know that the things you learn in school don't have anything to do with life."

"Dicto Simpliciter," she said, wagging her finger at me playfully.

That did it. I leaped to my feet, bellowing like a bull. "Will you or will you not go steady with me?"

"I will not," she replied.

"Why not?" I demanded.

"Because this afternoon I promised Petey Bellows that I would go steady with him."

I reeled back, overcome with the infamy of it. After he promised, after he made a deal, after he shook my hand! "The rat!" I shrieked, kicking up great chunks of turf. "You can't go with him, Polly. He's a liar. He's a cheat. He's a rat."

"Poisoning the Well," said Polly, "and stop shouting. I think shouting must be a fallacy too."

With an immense effort of will, I modulated my voice. "All right," I said. "You're a logician. Let's look at this thing logically. How could you choose Petey Bellows over me? Look at me—a brilliant student, a tremendous intellectual, a man with an assured future. Look at Petey—a knothead, a jitterbug, a guy who'll never know where his next meal is coming from. Can you give me one logical reason why you should go steady with Petey Bellows?"

"I certainly can," declared Polly. "He's got a raccoon coat."

Dobie Gillis manipulates

THE MOCK GOVERNOR

and has that worthy eating out of his hand

BY MAX SHULMAN

I FIRST SAW HER in Professor Pomfritt's political science class. In a sweater. When the class was over, I came up to her. "I'll get right to the point," I said. "I love you."

"You kill me," she said.

"You are the most beautiful woman in the freshman class," I said.

"You knock me out," she said.

"Possibly in the whole University of Minnesota," I said.

"You fracture me," she said.

"Take me to meet your folks," I said.

"They're on a world cruise," she said. "I'm living with my uncle."

"Take me to meet him."

"He won't like you."

"He'll like me."

"You don't know my uncle."

"I know this: he must be beautiful to have such a beautiful niece."

"You got rocks in your head," she said.

"I got a convertible too."

"A convertible head?"

"No, a convertible coupé. Let's go."

We went. We parked down by the riverbank and necked for a couple of hours. Then she said, "My name is Pearl McBride."

"How do you do," I said. "I'm Dobie Gillis."

"How do you do," she said. "What time is it?"

"A quarter to seven."

"Holy smoke, I'm late for dinner. Get me home quick, Dobie. The last time a boy brought me home late my uncle tore off a garage door and broke it over his head."

"Listen," I said speeding away, "when I get in front of your house, I'll slow down and you jump off."

"Nonsense. You're coming in and meet my uncle."

"But," I trembled, "a garage door—"

"Unless," she said, "you endear yourself to my uncle, our romance will never blossom. You don't want that, do you?"

I looked at her curly blond hair, at her big blue eyes, at her rose-red lips, at her sweater. "No," I said truthfully.

"Then you'll have to face my uncle. He's really not

so tough. He's a pushover for flattery. Give him some sweet talk."

"About what?" I asked.

"He's in the construction business. Talk about that."

"I don't know anything about construction."

"You've watched excavations, haven't you?"

"No," I said. "I get dizzy."

"Talk politics to him," Pearl suggested. "He's got an idea that he wants to be governor of Minnesota."

"A commendable ambition. What are his qualifications?"

"A strong handshake," she said.

"Anything else?"

"He smokes cigars and he talks real loud."

"Clearly the man for the job," I said.

"He's been sending up trial balloons, letting it be known around town that he's available for the nomination."

"Silence, mostly. Occasionally some giggles."

"What's happened?" I asked.

We pulled up in front of her house, a six-story concrete bunker with stained-glass windows. "My uncle had some cement left over from a dam he built," she explained.

"How about the windows?"

"Left over from a church. Come on."

"Wait, Pearl," I said, clutching the steering wheel, "perhaps it would be better if I came back tomorrow."

"Come on." She pulled me up the path by my necktie. "Don't forget—flatter him."

The front door opened and out came a livid man about eight feet all. "Where have you been?" he thundered.

"This is Dobie Gillis," said Pearl. "My uncle, Emmett McBride."

I extended a panicky hand. "I am proud, sir," I squeaked, "to meet the next governor of our state."

For a moment he stared at me. Then his hard red face relaxed. He gave my hand a cartilage-mashing shake. "Come in," he rumbled, "come in."

"You're doing fine," Pearl whispered as we entered.

"Pearl," said McBride, "why haven't you had Dobie over here before?"

"We just met this afternoon," said Perl, "in a political science class. Dobie is majoring in political science. He thinks politics is the highest pursuit of man, don't you, Dobie?"

"Except maybe construction," I replied.

Pearl beamed. McBride beamed. I beamed. We beamed all three.

"Sit down, Dobie," McBride invited. "Do you smoke cigars?"

"No, sir," I said, "but I admire a man who does."

He lit a Perfecto the size of my forearm. "Now what's all this talk about my being governor?"

"It's all over town, sir."

"Really?"

I prodded him playfully in the ribs. "Now don't pretend," I said with a smile, "that you haven't heard about it."

He chuckled, causing the dinner plates in the next room to rattle. "Well," he admitted, "I know that some of my many friends have been talking about it, but I haven't given them any encouragement."

A note of alarm came into my voice. "Sir, you *will* accept the nomination, won't you?"

"Well, I don't know," he said, dropping a mound of ashes on his vest.

I seized one of his thumbs with my two hands. "But you have to!"

"I don't know. I'm a very busy man, you know."

"You have to," I cried. "It's your duty to the people. Today, as never before, the people need leadership. You cannot shirk the responsibility. Say you'll accept, Mr. McBride. Say you will."

"Yes," he said simply.

"Perhaps," said Pearl, twinkling, "Dobie will stay for dinner."

"Of course he will," McBride declared. "Pearl, go tell Cook to set an extra place."

Pearl danced merrily into the kitchen.

"I'd offer you a drink," said McBride, "but I don't keep liquor in the house."

"Oh, that's all right," I said, noticing six bottles of bourbon through the half-open door of a cabinet.

"Man in public life has to be careful, you know," he said.

"Of course."

"Not that I miss it," he continued. "I live a very simple life—plain, wholesome food, a good book in the evening, fishing in the summer in our glorious lakes, hunting in the fall in our glorious woods—"

"What do you hunt?" I asked.

"Glorious deer," replied McBride.

"That must be fun," I said. "All I've ever shot are glorious pheasants."

"Ah," he said passionately, "This state abounds with glorious game."

"It's got people too," I said.

"Glorious people," he said.

"Who deserve a glorious governor," I said.

"Dobie," he said.

"Mr. McBride," I said.

"Dinner," Pearl said.

We sat down to a plain wholesome meal of vichyssoise, lobster Newburgh, artichoke hearts, sirloin Chateaubriand, button mushrooms, and peach melba.

After this snack I asked McBridge whether I could take Pearl out for a little while.

"Of course, son," he belched, "but be careful with my little girl." He rose laboriously from his chair and put a Neanderthal paw on her shoulder. "My little girl," he bellowed tenderly. "I like to think of Pearl as my own daughter. I've never had any children of my own." He sighed mightily. "Oh, I can't complain. Life's been good to me. But I think I'd trade all this"—his arm swept around the room, indicating a quarter of a million dollars' worth of overstuffed furniture—"for a child of my own. But that's life, I guess." He blew his big red nose.

"Tough," I said.

"Dobie," he said, "I want you to be the first to have one of these." From his breast pocket he removed a McBride for Governor sticker. "Paste it on your windshield."

"How can I thank you enough?" I said.

"Don't try. Run along now and be sure to have Pearl home by ten. Or else," he chuckled, "I will drive you into the ground like a wicket."

I saw him lumbering toward the bourbon as we left. In the car Pearl said, "Now, that wasn't so hard, was it?"

"No," I answered, "but just the same, I'm going to get you home by ten. No sense crowding our luck."

"All right, dear. What shall we do?"

"How about a movie? There's supposed to be a very unusual picture at the Bijou. It *isn't* told in flashback."

"It isn't?" said Pearl. "Then how is it told?"

"They just start at the beginning of the story and go right straight through to the end."

"Revolutionary," said Pearl.

I headed the car toward the Bijou. "Tomorrow night," I suggested, "let's go canoeing."

"Marvy," said Pearl.

"And Friday night we'll go dancing."

"Terrif," said Pearl.

I took her hand. She smiled. I smiled back. Our eyes met. The car ran up on the sidewalk and into a barbershop.

At 11:35 that evening Pearl and I limped up the

walk to her house. She had a few yards of tape on her hand. I was uninjured except for a couple of civil and criminal actions pending against me.

McBride came bounding out the door like a big fat jack-in-the-box. "What happened?" he roared.

"Flatter him," Pearl whispered to me and ducked prudently into the house.

"What happened?" repeated McBride, grabbing a handful of my shirt and holding me out at arm's length.

"Oh, sir," I cried, "I can hardly wait until you're governor. The roads in this state are deplorable."

"What," he gritted, "happened?"

"What we need," I said, "is a governor who is also an expert in construction. That's what we need."

He put me down slowly. "What happened?" he asked again.

"You should have seen that disgraceful hole right in the middle of the street," I said. "We'd have both been killed if I hadn't had the presence of mind to drive into a nearby barbershop. Oh, how I wish it was next fall and you were in office."

He rubbed his head for a minute. "How's Pearl?" he asked at length.

"Just a scratch, thank heaven. But there's no telling what will happen to our citizens on these treacherous roads until you are elected and straighten things out."

He sat down on the stoop. "Dobie, listen. You got to be more careful with Pearl. If anything like this ever happens again, I'll—"

"Yes, sir," I interrupted quickly. "I'll be very careful. Good night."

"Good night," he mumbled.

The next night in the canoe, the water lapping softly on the gunwales, the moon bright on Pearl's bandages, she said: "You are a genius."

"Pshaw," I said.

"What a great talent you have for handling people."

"I've got another talent too," I said.

"What?"

"I can tell time. Pearl, it's 9:35. I've got to paddle back to the boat dock and then drive you home by ten. I don't think your uncle Emmett can be pushed much further."

"We'll go in a minute, Dobie. Now lean back."

"Pearl, I think we better leave now."

"Just a few seconds more."

"No."

"Aw, Dobie."

"Well, just a few seconds."

In just a few seconds it was 9:50 and I was frantic. "We'll never make it," I wailed.

"Don't be silly," she said. "It will take you three minutes to get to the boat dock and seven minutes to drive me home. We'll make it."

"Three minutes to the boat dock? You're off your trolley. It took me fifteen minutes to paddle out here."

"Of course," she said. "You were sitting down. Can't make any time that way. Stand up and paddle."

"Stand up?" I asked, aghast.

"Sure. Come on, get up."

"But you're not supposed to stand up in a boat."

"A myth," she sail lightly. "Indians did it all the time." I got up shakily. "I'll tip over the boat," I said.

"Nonsense," said Pearl as I tipped over the boat.

It was a little after midnight when I brought Pearl home in a blanket. "Good luck," she sneezed and ran past Uncle Emmett into the house.

"It's shocking," I yelled as McBride chased me around the lawn, "the things that go on in this state. Do you know," I asked, vaulting an iron deer, "that there are boats for rent that are not seaworthy? Things," I said, flattening a tulip bed, "have gotten out of hand. What we need in this state is a strong man in the governor's mansion. A man subject neither," I said, capsizing a deck chair, "to fear nor favoritism; a man who will stamp out corruption in high and low places; a man"—he was getting pretty winded—"who will protect the weal of the people; a man stern but just; in short"—he sat abruptly on the grass—"a man like you."

"Dobie," he gasped, "now what have you done?"

"An accident," I replied. "The kind of accident that will not be allowed to happen in your administration."

"Dobie, I'm a patient man—"

"An admirable quality in a governor."

"But this is positively the last time that—"

"Yes, sir. It will never happen again."

"If it does, I'll—"

"Well, I'd better get home now and do some studying for that fascinating political science course. We're having a fascinating test tomorrow. Good night."

He didn't answer.

The next night at the dance I was firm. "We are leaving," I told Pearl, "at nine-thirty."

"But," she protested, "it only takes ten minutes to drive home."

I shook my head and repeated, "We are leaving at nine-thirty."

And promptly at nine-thirty we left. I drove carefully away from the curb. I signaled for all turns, stopped for all lights, passed no cars, kept both hands on the wheel, and never let the speedometer needle get above 25. But all these precautions notwithstanding, halfway home tragedy struck. The motor coughed and died.

I displayed admirable calm. "Pearl," I said quietly, "let us keep our heads. It is twenty minutes before ten. We are a mile from your house. We will get out of the car and walk."

"In these shoes?" asked Pearl, pointing at a pair of flimsy gold things with an arch like a ski slide.

"You can take them off and go barefoot. Or, if you prefer, I'll carry you. In either case, we are leaving immediately. Come on."

"Aren't you even going to lift up the hood and look at the motor?" she asked. "Everybody always does that before they abandon a car."

"I don't know any more about motors than I do about the Koran," I said. "Let's go."

She got out of the car. "Come on, Dobie, let's take

a look at the motor. Maybe we'll see something loose or something. Come on, Dobie. It will only take a second to look."

"Oh, all right," I surrendered.

"Goody," she said. "I love to look at motors."

I opened the hood and we peered inside. "You have a nice motor, Dobie," she said.

"Thanks," I murmured.

"All those wires and bolts and things."

"All right, Pearl. We'll start walking now."

"Just a minute, Dobie. I think I see something loose."

"Never mind, Pearl. Let's get going."

"No, Dobie. Look at this little thing over by that little thing."

I looked at this little thing over by that little thing, and sure enough it did seem to have come loose. I fastened it with a pin that seemed to be made for that purpose.

"Now start the car, Dobie. I'll watch."

After extracting a promise from Pearl that we'd leave instantly on foot if the car failed to start, I got back behind the wheel. I stepped on the starter, remembering just too late that the tip of her long, frilly sleeve was resting on the fan belt. There was a ripping and tearing and a pinwheel of flying taffeta.

"It started! It started!" she cried, standing in the street in her dance set.

Uncle Emmett was nowhere in sight when I escorted Pearly up the path, she rakishly dressed in a seat cover.

She slipped into the house. I started tiptoeing back to the car. Then I saw him. Or, rather, I saw a garage door racing toward me like an express train. I executed a twenty-foot standing broad jump, landed on all fours, left the knees of my rented tux on the sidewalk, leaped into the car, and set a world's record for speed in first gear.

For the next several days no moon shone on our romance. We saw one another only by daylight, and when I took her home, I dropped her off a safe six blocks away. It was very unsatisfactory. To our credit it must be said that we worked hard on plans to win over Uncle Emmett, but the best of these plans—for me to grow a mustache and call on Pearl under an assumed name—was none too good. Things looked black.

Then one day before our political science class, Pearl ran up to me in a state of high excitement. I could almost hear her brain clicking. "I've got an idea," she said.

"It better be good."

"It's perfect. Listen, Dobie, what does Uncle Emmett want most in the world?"

"To hit me with a garage door."

She made an impatient gesture. "I'm serious. What does he want most?"

"To be governor."

"Exactly. And there's nothing he won't do for anybody who can make him governor." She prodded my chest with her forefinger. "Dobie, you are going to do it."

"It's too dirty a trick on the people of Minnesota," I said. "I won't do it."

"I don't mean real governor," she said. "I mean mock governor."

"What's that?" I asked. "Someone who goes around mocking the governor?"

"You don't understand," she began as the bell rang for the start of the political science class.

"Let's cut class," I suggested, "and you tell me all about it."

She said, "No, we've got to go to class. That's part of the plan."

I shrugged and followed her in. For an hour I nodded through Professor Pomfritt's lecture. When class was over I asked Pearl, "Now what?"

"Now we go up and see Professor Pomfritt."

"What are we going to do with him?"

"First we'll flatter him."

"That," I said, "seems to be the standard approach with you."

I followed Pearl up to the lectern where Professor Pomfritt was gathering up his notes and wondering how he was going to live out the year on his salary.

"Professor Pomfritt," said Pearl, "we want to tell you how much we've been enjoying your lectures. Haven't we, Dobie?"

"Yeah," I said.

"Well, thank you, thank you," crowed the professor, his little old eyes crinkling with pleasure.

"We think you give the most stimulating lectures

on campus. Don't we, Dobie?"

"Yeah," I said.

"You should have heard me twenty years ago when my lecture notes were still legible," said the professor.

"Nobody," said Pearl, "can accuse you of being an ivory tower professor. Political science is a living, breathing subject, and the way you teach it is real and vital. Isn't it, Dobie?"

"Yeah," I said.

"Well," chirped the professor. "Well, well, well. I'd ask you up to my rooms for tea only I don't have any tea. However, if you'd like a cup of warm water—"

"No, thanks," said Pearl. "We got another class."

"Bless me, so do I!" exclaimed Professor Pomfritt and started away. "Come up and chat again."

Pearl grabbed his frayed elbow. "There's one thing, Professor. As you know, a new governor will be elected in Minnesota next fall, and there's been a lot of talk about it among the students."

"So that's what they all talk about while I'm lecturing," mused the professor.

Pearl yanked his elbow, shredding the ancient tweed. "This can't wait," she said urgently. "The talk about the election is getting very heated. I'm afraid the students may come to blows."

"Dear me," said the professor. "What's to be done?"

"If I may make a suggestion," she replied, "why not hold a mock election in class? It will be a good practical exercise in political science and it will pacify the students."

"Your inspirational teaching," said Pearl, taking a deep breath, "has got us all so interested in politics that we can't think of anything else."

"We must talk about this some more," said Professor Pomfritt. "Come over tomorrow afternoon. I will borrow some tea leaves from my Chinese laundryman."

The professor looked doubtful. "I don't know. I've never done anything like this before."

"I'm sure," Pearl continued, "that there will be a lot of publicity for our mock election. This being an election year, the newspapers will certainly send reporters."

"Newspapers?" said the professor, brightening. "Ah, good. The last time I had my name in the newspapers I got a raise. It was in 1927. I fainted at the Lindbergh parade. Malnutrition, the papers said, and the dean was forced to increase my salary."

"Then it's all settled?" asked Pearl.

"Very well. But you'll have to help me organize this function. I know so little about these things."

"Don't you worry," Pearl reassured him. "I'll take care of everything. We'll have the mock election on Friday. Just leave all the details to me. Goodbye, Professor, and we wish we had more teachers like you, don't we, Dobie?"

"Yeah," I said.

We left the professor and went outside. "Now," said Pearl, "let's get busy. I'll go around to the newspapers and see that they send reporters. You start working on your speech."

"My speech?"

"You are going to nominate Uncle Emmett with a great speech, a stirring speech, a magnificent speech."

"About him? That's a good trick."

"You can do it, Dobie."

"I can?" I said uncertainly. "Well, I'll try. Tell me something about him. Maybe he has an attractive side that I haven't noticed. What about his education?"

"He quit school in the fifth grade," said Pearl. "He was eighteen and so big that all the other kids used to laugh at him."

"Hm," I said. "Well, maybe that's not so bad. So he didn't have an education. He went to work, rose from the ranks, rags to riches. That's good stuff—a self-made man."

"No," said Pearl. "His father left him the business."

"Maybe," I suggested, "I could say that he's real strong."

Pearl shook her head.

"I doubt," I said, "that I can get him any votes by telling how much he eats."

Pearl had an idea. "Why don't you say something like this? In times of reconstruction we need a construction man."

"And in times of retrenchment we need a trencherman."

"Wait," said Pearl. "You've given me an angle. Reconstruction and retrenchment. For reconstruction, a construction man. For retrenchment, a businessman. Even if Uncle Emmett did inherit the company, you can show that it was his own business ability that made it pay off. He's made scads of money. I'll dig up some facts and figures. You will cite evidence to prove what he has built and how much he has earned. A construction man for reconstruction. A businessman for retrenchment. Uncle Emmett, you will demonstrate, is both."

"It might work," I allowed.

"It *will* work and Uncle Emmett will read all about your speech in the papers and he will welcome you back like a long lost son and we can start necking at night again."

"What are we waiting for?" I said, rubbing my hands briskly. "Let's get started."

By election time on Friday we were ready. Pearl had alerted the newspapers. I had composed an eloquent speech based on data that Pearl had copied from a ledger she found in her uncle's desk. Our plans were well laid and synchronized. We were confident.

Pearl, the self-appointed chairwoman, stepped to the lectern. At a table on the side of the room sat a dozen reporters, about whom Professor Pomfritt, with new leather patches on his elbows, hovered like a genial bee. The students were in a festive mood. Pearl rapped for silence.

"Nominations," she said, "are now in order."

I stood and was recognized. "Ladies and gentlemen," said I, loud and clear, "I want to tell you about a fellow Minnesotan named Emmett McBride. Emmett McBride is in the construction business. In the last few years

Emmett McBride has constructed the following edifices at the following profits: The First National Bank of Minneapolis—$1,583,087; the St. Cloud-Chaska highway—$987,590; the Rochester reservoir—$798,679; the Sauk Center viaduct—$807,234; the Bemidji causeway—$694,589."

"Hooray!" shouted Pearl from the chair.

"I mention these figures," I said, "to prove two things. First that Emmett McBride is a construction man. Second, that Emmett McBride is a businessman."

"Hooray!" shouted Pearl from the chair.

"In these parlous days of reconstruction and retrenchment," I went on, "do we want a politician in the governor's mansion?"

"No!" shouted Pearl from the chair.

"Do we want a theorist in the governor's mansion?"

"No!" shouted Pearl from the chair.

"What do we want in the governor's mansion?" I asked.

"A construction man and a businessman," shouted Pearl from the chair.

"Exactly," I said. "And since we can't have two governors, we must find a man who is both a construction man and a businessman. Emmett McBride is both. In these parlous days of reconstruction and retrenchment, we want Emmett McBride in the governor's mansion, that's who we want."

"Hooray!" shouted Pearl from the chair, and from the students the cry came back, "Hooray!"

"Few of you," I said, "have ever heard of Emmett

McBride. He has never been a candidate for office. It is fitting that the discovery of Emmett McBride should be made at this university which has been the scene of so many other great discoveries. Here is the source of progress in this state. The people look to us for leadership. Let us supply that leadership. Let us elect Emmett McBride!"

Before the mounting cheers could get out of control, Pearl shouted, "I move that McBride be elected by acclamation."

"You can't make a motion from the chair," cried some finicky parliamentarian, but his voice was lost as the entire assemblage in full-throated uproar acclaimed Emmett McBride the victor.

Then I was hoisted on several shoulders and carried around the room. "Uncle Emmett will love you," yelled Pearl as I was carried past her.

"How about his niece?" I asked as I circled her the second time and she nodded energetically and blew kisses.

"I'll be over tomorrow morning—after he's had a chance to read the papers," I said the third time around.

It was all on the front pages the next morning, and I drove to Pearl's house whistling all the way. I walked boldly up the path, threw open the door without knocking, and called cheerily, "Where is lovable old Uncle Emmett?"

Pearl, lying prone on the living-room sofa, lifted a tear-stained face. She looked at me for an instant, then scrambled to her feet. "Run for your life," she cried.

"Leave the city. Leave the state. Leave the country if possible."

"What's the gag?" I asked, mystified.

"Hurry! Uncle Emmett will be at home any minute. He's already raised his bail."

"Bail?"

"You read the papers, Dobie—all those figures you gave about Uncle Emmett's profits."

"So?"

"So they arrested him this morning for income tax evasion."

LEONARD Q. ROSS (1908-   )

. . . was an immigrant from Poland—which accounts for his loving sympathy for the plight of the foreigner in America.

With a marvelous ear for language, Ross has immortalized the problems of the immigrant in The Education of H*Y*M*A*N K*A*P*L*A*N, *a best seller. This classic was followed by* The Return of H*Y*M*A*N K*A*P*L*A*N, *a well-received sequel.*

This encounter between

MR. KAPLAN
AND VOCABULARY

stood the teacher on his ear

THE PITCHER HANGS
COCKEYE

"VOCABULARY!" said Mr. Parkhill. "Above all, we must work on vocabulary."

He was probably right. For the students in the beginners' grade, vocabulary was a dire and pressing need. Spelling, after all, was not of such immediate importance to people who did little writing during their daily lives. Grammar? They needed the substance—words, phrases, idioms—to which grammar might be applied. Pronunciation? Mr. Parkhill had come to the reluctant conclusion that for some of them accurate pronunciation was a near impossibility. Take Mr. Kaplan, for example. Mr. Kaplan was a willing, an earnest, aye! an enthusiastic pupil. And yet, despite Mr. Parkhill's tireless tutelage, Mr. Kaplan referred to the most celebrated of movie lovers as "Clock Gebble," who, it appeared, showed a fine set of teeth "veneer he greens." Mr. Kaplan, when asked to use "heaven" in a sentence, had replied promptly, "In sommer, ve all heaven a fine time."

Yes, vocabulary—that, Mr. Parkhill thought, was the greatest need.

". . . And so tonight I shall write a list of new, useful words on the blackboard. To each student I shall assign three words. Write a sentence in your notebooks using each word. Make sure you have no mistakes. You may use your dictionaries, if you wish. Then go to the board and copy your three sentences for class analysis."

The class was impressed and pleased. Miss Mitnick's ordinarily shy expression changed to one of eager expectancy. Mrs. Moskowitz, simple soul that she was, prepared her notebook with stolid solemnity. And Mr. Kaplan, in the middle of the front row, took out his box of crayons, smiled more broadly than ever (a chance to use his crayons always intensified Mr. Kaplan's natural euphoria), turned to a fresh page in his notebook, and printed, slowly and with great love:

VOCAPULERY

(Prectice in Book. Then Going to Blackb. and putting on.)

by

H*Y*M*A*N   K*A*P*L*A*N

For the title he chose purple crayon; for the methodological observation in parentheses, orange; for the "by," yellow. His name he printed, fondly, as always:

in red and blue and flamboyant green. As he handled the crayons Mr. Kaplan smiled with the sweet serenity of one in direct communication with his Muse.

Mr. Parkhill assigned three words to each student and the beginners' grade went into action. Lips pursed, brows wrinkled, distant looks appeared in thoughtful eyes; heads were scratched, chins stroked, dictionaries fluttered. Mr. Kaplan tackled his three words with gusto: *pitcher, fascinate, university.* Mr. Parkhill noticed that Mr. Kaplan's cerebration was accompanied by strange sounds: he pronounced each word, and tried fitting it into a sentence, in a whisper which could be heard halfway across the room. He muttered the entire process of his reasoning. Mr. Kaplan, it seemed, thought only in dialogue with his other self. There was something uncanny about it.

"Pitcher . . . pitcher," Mr. Kaplan whispered "Is maybe a pitcher for milk? Is maybe a pitcher on de vall —*art!* Aha! Two minninks! "Plizz take milk fromm de pitcher.' Fine! 'De pitcher hengs cockeye.' Also fine! Pitcher . . . pitcher."

This private colloquy was not indulged in without a subtle design, for Mr. Kaplan watched Mr. Parkhill's facial expressions carefully out of the corner of his eye as he whispered to himself. Mr. Kaplan hoped to discover which interpretation of "pitcher" was acceptable. But Mr. Parkhill had long ago learned to beware of Mr. Kaplan's strategies; he preserved a stern facial immobility as Mr. Kaplan's stage whispers floated through the classroom.

When Mr. Kaplan had finished his three sentences he reread them proudly, nodded happily to Mr. Parkhill (who, though pretending to be watching Miss Schneiderman at the blackboard, was watching Mr. Kaplan out of the corner of *his* eye), and went to the board. He whispered the sentences aloud as he copied them. Ecstasy illuminated his face.

"Well," said Mr. Parkhill after all the students had transcribed their work, "let's start at this end. Mr. Bloom, I think?"

Mr. Bloom read his sentences quickly:

She *declined* the money.

In her red hat she falt *conspicuous.*

Last Saturday, I saw a *remarkable* show.

"Excellent!" said Mr. Parkhill. "Are there any questions?" There were no questions. Mr. Parkhill corrected "falt" and the exercise continued. On the whole, all went surprisingly well. Except for those of Mrs. Moskowitz, who worked havoc with "niggardly" ("It was a *niggardly* night"), the sentences were quite good. Mr. Parkhill was delighted. The experiment in vocabulary-building was proving a decided success. At last Mr. Kaplan's three sentences came up.

"Mr. Kaplan is next, I believe." There was a note of caution in Mr. Parkhill's voice.

Mr. Kaplan went to the board. "Mine foist void, ladies an' gantleman," he announced, smiling (Mr. Kaplan always did things with a certain bravado), "is 'pitcher.' So de santence is: 'Oh, how beauriful is dis *pitcher.*'"

Mr. Parkhill saw that Mr. Kaplan had neatly strad-
dled two words by a deliberately noncommittal usage.
"Er— Mr. Kaplan. The word is 'p-i-t-c-h-e-r,' not
'p-i-c-t-u-r-e.' "

Too late did Mr. Parkhill realize that he had given
Mr. Kaplan the clue he had been seeking.

"Mr. Pockheel," Mr. Kaplan replied with consum-
mate simplicity, "dis void *is* 'p-i-t-c-h-e-r.' "

"But when you say, 'Oh, how *beautiful* this pitcher
is,' " said Mr. Parkhill, determined to force Mr. Kaplan to the wall, "you suggest—"

"Ah!" Mr. Kaplan murmured, with a tolerant smile.
"In som houses is even de *pitchers* beauriful."

"Read your next sentence, Mr. Kaplan."

Mr. Kaplan went on, smiling. "De sacond void,
ladies an' gantleman, is 'fascinate'—an' believe me is a
planty hod void! So is mine santence: 'In India is all
kinds snake-fescinators.' "

"You are thinking of snake-*charmers.*" (Mr. Kaplan seemed to have taken the dictionary's description
of "fascinate" too literally.) "Try 'fascinate' in another
sentence, please."

Mr. Kaplan gazed ceilingward with a masterful insouciance, one eye half-closed. Then he ventured: "You
fescinate me."

Mr. Parkhill hurried Mr. Kaplan on to his last word.

"Toid void, faller-students, is 'univoisity.' De santence usink dis void: 'Elaven yiss is married mine vife
an' minesalf, so is time commink for our tvalft *univoisity.' "

It was the opportunity for which Miss Mitnick had been waiting. "Mr. Kaplan mixes up two words," she said. "He means 'anniversary.' 'University' is a high college—the *highest* college."

Mr. Kaplan listened to this unwelcome correction with a fine sufferance. Then he arched his eyebrows and said, "You got right, Mitnick. Hau Kay! So I'll givink anodder santence: 'Som pipple didn't have aducation in a *univoisity*' "—he glanced meaningfully at Miss Mitnick—" 'but just de same, dey havink efter elaven yiss de tvalft *annivoisery*.' "

With this retort courteous Mr. Kaplan took his seat. Through the next few recitations he was strangely silent. He did not bother to offer a correction of Miss Kowalski's spectacular misuse of "guess." ("Turn out the guess.") He did not as much as volunteer an opinion on Miss Hirschfield's "The cat omits a cry." For all his proud smile it was clear that Mr. Kaplan had suffered a deep hurt: like a smoldering cinder in his soul lay the thought of his humiliation at the mundane hands of one Rose Mitnick. He smiled as bravely as ever, but his silence was ominous. He seemed to be waiting, waiting. . . .

"Miss Mitnick, please," said Mr. Parkhill. A flame leaped into Mr. Kaplan's eyes.

Miss Mitnick's first sentence was *"Enamel* is used for painting chairs." Before she could read it Mr. Kaplan's voice rang out in triumph.

"Mistake by Mitnick! Ha! Mit *enimals* she is painting chairs? Ha!"

"The word is *'enamel,'* " said Mr. Parkhill coldly. "Not 'animal.' "

Rebuffed, Mr. Kaplan let Miss Mitnick's reading of that sentence, and her next, go unchallenged. But the flame burned in his eyes again when she read her final effort: "The prisoner stood in the *dock*."

"Well," suggested Mr. Parkhill, before Mr. Kaplan, squirming with excitement in his chair, could offer a rash correction, "that's one way to use the word. The English use it that way. But there is a—er—more common usage. Can you use 'dock' in a more familiar meaning, Miss Mitnick?"

Miss Mitnick was silent.

"Anyone?"

"I like roast *duck!*" cried Mr. Kaplan promptly.

"*Dock!*" Mr. Parkhill said severely. "Not *duck!*" Once again Mr. Kaplan bowed to a cruel fate.

" 'Dock' isn't hard," said Mr. Parkhill encouragingly. "I'll give you a hint, class. Each of you, in coming to America, has had *direct experience with a dock*." He smiled almost gaily, and waited.

The class went into that coma which signified thought, searching its collective memory of "coming to America." Mrs. Moskowitz closed her eyes as the recollection of her sea-sickness surged over her like a wave, and searched her memory no more. Mr. Kaplan, desperate to make the kill, whispered his associations tensely: " 'Dock . . . Commink to America . . . boat . . . feesh . . . big vaves . . . cremps."

It was clear they were getting nowhere. (Mr. Norman Bloom, indeed, had forgotten all about "dock" in his sweet recollection of the pinochle game on the boat when he had won four and a half dollars.)

"Well, I'll make it even easier," said Mr. Parkhill lightly. "Where did your boats *land?*"

"New York!" cried Mr. Kaplan eagerly.

Mr. Parkhill cleared his throat. "Yes—of course. But I mean—"

A cry of joy came from the lips of Hyman Kaplan. "I got him! Ufcawss! *'Dock!'* Plain an' tsimple! Ha!" He shot a look of triumph toward Miss Mitnick. "I'm soprize so high-cless a student like Mitnick, she knows all abot fency voids like 'univoisities' and 'annivoiseries,' she shouldn't know a leetle void like 'dock'!"

Something in Mr. Parkhill warned him. Not for a moment could he believe that Mr. Kaplan's confidence and enthusiasm were authentic indications of a correct answer. Mr. Parkhill would have preferred that some other student try a sentence with "dock." But no one volunteered.

"Very well, Mr. Kaplan," he said, staring at his fingers, as if to break the impact of Mr. Kaplan's contribution.

Mr. Kaplan rose, inspiration in his eyes. His smile was so wide that his face seemed to be one ecstatic cavern. He cast majestic glances to both sides, as if reading the tribute in the faces of his fellow-students. Then he said, in one triumphant breath, "Hollo, Doc!"

Peace fell upon the room. Through the windows, from far away, there came the muted rumble of the

Third Avenue elevated. The features of Abraham Lincoln on the wall took on, somehow, a softer understanding. But Mr. Parkhill was aware only of a strange and unaccountable ringing in his ears ("Hello, Doc!" . . . "Hello, Doc!") and, while shaking his head sadly to show Mr. Kaplan that he was wrong, he thought to himself with feverish persistence, "Vocabulary. Above all, vocabulary."

O. HENRY (1862-1910)

...whose real name was William Sidney Porter, served many apprenticeships before turning to writing. He worked as a drugstore clerk, bookkeeper, draftsman, and bank teller—moving from his birthplace in Greensboro, North Carolina to Texas, then to Ohio, on to Pennsylvania, and finally to New York.

Sentenced to five years in prison for embezzlement, he began to write when in jail. There he assumed the pen name of O. Henry, perhaps suggested by the name of a prison guard, Orrin Henry.

He was only 48 when he died, but had turned out 600 pieces of fiction. His stories were published in noted magazines such as Cosmopolitan, Aimslee's, McClure's, *and* Munsey's *and his collected works number over 12 volumes. His view of the world, as expressed in his short stories, is ironic though not bitter. His writing is somewhat uneven and, at times, his phrasing is somewhat forced. But his literary shortcomings, whatever they are, are overlooked because of his good sense of things and his clever unexpected endings.*

A con game's going on, with

JEFF PETERS AS A
PERSONAL MAGNET

JEFF PETERS has been engaged in as many schemes for making money as there are recipes for cooking rice in Charleston, S. C.

Best of all I like to hear him tell of his earlier days when he sold liniments and cough cures on street corners, living hand to mouth, heart to heart with the people, throwing heads or tails with fortune for his last coin.

I struck Fisher Hill, Arkansaw (said he) in buckskin suit, moccasins, long hair and a thirty-carat diamond ring that I got from an actor in Texarkana. I don't know what he ever did with the pocket knife I swapped him for it.

I was Dr. Waugh-hoo, the celebrated Indian medi-

cine man. I carried only one best bet just then, and that
was Resurrection Bitters. It was made of life-giving
plants and herbs accidentally discovered by Ta-qua-la,
the beautiful wife of the chief of the Choctaw Nation,
while gathering truck to garnish a platter of boiled dog
for the annual corn dance.

Business hadn't been good at the last town, so I only
had five dollars. I went to the Fisher Hill druggist and
he credited me for a half gross of eight ounce bottles
and corks. I had the labels and ingredients in my valise,
left over from the last town. Life began to look rosy
again after I got in my hotel room with the water running from the tap, and the Resurrection Bitters lining
up on the table by the dozen.

Fake? No, sir. There was two dollars' worth of fluid
extract of cinchona and a dime's worth of aniline in
that half-gross of bitters. I've gone through towns years
afterwards and had folks ask for 'em again.

I hired a wagon that night and commenced selling
the bitters on Main Street. Fisher Hill was a low, ma-
larial town; and a compound hypothetical pneumo-
cardiac anti-scorbutic tonic was just what I diagnosed
the crowd as needing. The bitters started off like sweet-
breads-on-toast at a vegetarian dinner. I had sold two
dozen at fifty cents apiece when I felt somebody pull
my coat tail. I knew what that meant; so I climbed
down and sneaked a five-dollar bill into the hand of a
man with a German silver star on his lapel.

"Constable," says I, "it's a fine night."

"Have you got a city license," he asks, "to sell this

illegitimate essence of spooju that you flatter by the name of medicine?"

"I have not," says I. "I didn't know you had a city. If I can find it tomorrow I'll take one out if it's necessary."

"I'll have to close you up till you do," says the constable.

I quit selling and went back to the hotel. I was talking to the landlord about it.

"Oh, you won't stand no show in Fisher Hill," says he. "Dr. Hoskins, the only doctor here, is a brother-in-law of the Mayor, and they won't allow no fake doctors to practice in town."

"I don't practice medicine," says I, "I've got a State peddler's license, and I take out a city one wherever they demand it."

I went to the Mayor's office the next morning and they told me he hadn't showed up yet. They didn't know when he'd be down. So Doc Waugh-hoo hunches down again in a hotel chair and lights a jimpson-weed regalia, and waits.

By and by a young man in a blue necktie slips into the chair next to me and asks the time.

"Half-past ten," says I, "and you are Andy Tucker. I've seen you work. Wasn't it you that put up the Great Cupid Combination package on the Southern States. Let's see, it was a Chilian diamond engagement ring, a wedding ring, a potato masher, a bottle of soothing syrup and Dorothy Vernon—all for fifty cents."

Andy was pleased to hear that I remembered him.

He was a good street man; and he was more than that—
he respected his profession, and he was satisfied with
300 per cent profit. He had plenty of offers to go into
the illegitimate drug and garden seed business; but he
was never to be tempted off of the straight path.

I wanted a partner, so Andy and me agreed to go out
together. I told him about the situation on Fisher Hill
and how finances was low on account of the local mixture of politics and jalap. Andy had just got in on the
train that morning. He was pretty low himself, and
was going to canvass the town for a few dollars to build
a new battleship by popular subscription at Eureka
Springs. So we went out and sat on the porch and talked
it over.

The next morning at eleven o'clock when I was sitting there alone, an Uncle Tom shuffles into the hotel
and asked the doctor to come and see Judge Banks,
who, it seems, was the mayor and a mighty sick man.

"I'm no doctor," says I. "Why don't you go and get
the doctor?"

"Boss," says he. "Doc Hoskin am done gone twenty
miles in the country to see some sick persons. He's de
only doctor in de town, and Massa Banks am powerful
bad off. He sent me to ax you to please, suh, come."

"As man to man," says I, "I'll go and look him over."
So I put a bottle of Resurrection Bitters in my pocket
and goes up on the hill to the mayor's mansion, the finest house in town, with a mansard roof and two cast-
iron dogs on the lawn.

This Mayor Banks was in bed all but his whiskers

and feet. He was making internal noises that would have had everybody in San Francisco hiking for the parks. A young man was standing by the bed holding a cup of water.

"Doc," says the Mayor, "I'm awful sick. I'm about to die. Can't you do nothing for me?"

"Mr. Mayor," says I, "I'm not a regular preordained disciple of S. Q. Lapius, I never took a course in a medical college," says I. "I've just come as a fellow man to see if I could be of any assistance."

"I'm deeply obliged," says he. "Doc Waugh-hoo, this is my nephew, Mr. Biddle. He has tried to alleviate my distress, but without success. Oh, Lordy! Ow-ow-ow!" he sings out.

I nods at Mr. Biddle and sets down by the bed and feels the mayor's pulse. "Let me see your liver—your tongue, I mean," says I. Then I turns up the lids of his eyes and looks close at the pupils of 'em.

"How long have you been sick?" I asked.

"I was taken down—ow-ouch—last night," says the Mayor. "Gimme something for it, doc, won't you?"

"Mr. Fiddle," says I, "raise the window shade a bit, will you?"

"Biddle," says the young man. "Do you feel like you could eat some ham and eggs, Uncle James?"

"Mr. Mayor," says I, after laying my ear to his right shoulder blade and listening, "you've got a bad attack of super-inflammation of the right clavicle of the harpsichord!"

"Good Lord!" says he, with a groan. "Can't you rub

something on it, or set it or anything?"

I picks up my hat and starts for the door.

"You ain't going, doc?" says the Mayor with a howl. "You ain't going away and leave me to die with this—superfluity of the clapboards, are you?"

"Common humanity, Dr. Whoa-ha," says Mr. Biddle, "ought to prevent your deserting a fellow-human in distress."

Dr. Waugh-hoo, when you get through plowing," says I. And then I walks back to the bed and throws back my long hair.

"Mr. Mayor," says I, "there is only one hope for you. Drugs will do you no good. But there is another power higher yet, although drugs are high enough," says I.

"And what is that?" says he.

"Scientific demonstrations," says I. "The triumph of mind over sarsaparilla. The belief that there is no pain and sickness except what is produced when we ain't feeling well. Declare yourself in arrears. Demonstrate."

"What is this paraphernalia you speak of, Doc?" says the Mayor. "You ain't a Socialist, are you?"

"I am speaking," says I, "of the great doctrine of psychic financiering—of the enlightened school of long-distance, sub-conscientious treatment of fallacies and meningitis—of that wonderful indoor sport known as personal magnetism."

"Can you work it, Doc?" asks the Mayor.

"I'm one of the Sole Sanhedrims and Ostensible Hooplas of the Inner Pulpit," says I. "The lame talk and the blind rubber whenever I make a pass at 'em. I am a medium, a coloratura hypnotist and a spirituous control. It was only through me at the recent seances at Ann Arbor that the late president of the Vinegar Bitters Company could revisit the earth to communicate with his sister Jane. You see me peddling medicine on the streets," says I, "to the poor. I don't practice personal magnetism on them. I do not drag it in the dust," says I, "because they haven't got the dust."

"Will you treat my case?" asks the Mayor.

"Listen," says I. "I've had a good deal of trouble with medical societies everywhere I've been. I don't practice medicine. But, to save your life, I'll give you the psychic treatment if you'll agree as mayor not to push the license question."

"Of course I will," says he. "And now get to work, Doc, for them pains are coming on again."

"My fee will be $250.00 cure guaranteed in two treatments," says I.

"All right," says the Mayor. "I'll pay it. I guess my life's worth that much."

I sat down by the bed and looked him straight in the eye.

"Now," says I, "get your mind off the disease. You ain't sick. You haven't got a heart or a clavicle or a funny bone or brains or anything. You haven't got any pain. Declare error. Now you feel the pain that you didn't have leaving, don't you?"

"I do feel some little better, Doc," says the Mayor, "darned if I don't. Now state a few lies about my not having this swelling in my left side, and I think I could be propped up and have some sausage and buckwheat cakes."

I made a few passes with my hands.

"Now," says I, "the inflammation's gone. The right lobe of the perihelion has subsided. You're getting sleepy. You can't hold your eyes open any longer. For the present the disease is checked. Now, you are asleep."

The Mayor shut his eyes slowly and began to snore.

"You observe, Mr. Tiddle," says I, "the wonders of modern science."

"Biddle," says he. "When will you give uncle the rest of the treatment, Dr. Pooh-pooh?"

"Waugh-hoo," says I. "I'll come back at eleven to-morrow. When he wakes up give him eight drops of turpentine and three pounds of steak. Good morning."

The next morning I went back on time. "Well, Mr. Riddle," says I, when he opened the bedroom door, "and how is uncle this morning?"

"He seems much better," says the young man.

The Mayor's color and pulse was fine. I gave him another treatment, and he said the last of the pain left him.

"Now," says I, "you'd better stay in bed for a day or two, and you'll be all right. It's a good thing I hap-epned to be in Fisher Hill, Mr. Mayor," says I, "for all the remedies in the cornucopia that the regular schools of medicine use couldn't have saved you. And now that error has flew and pain proved a perjurer, let's allude to a cheerfuller subject—say the fee of $250.00.

No checks, please, I hate to write my name on the back of a check almost as bad as I do on the front."

"I've got the cash here," says the Mayor, pulling a pocketbook from under his pillow.

He counts out five fifty-dollar notes and holds 'em in his hand.

"Bring the receipt," he says to Biddle.

I signed the receipt and the Mayor handed me the money. I put it in my inside pocket careful.

"Now do your duty, officer," says the Mayor, grinning much unlike a sick man.

Mr. Biddle lays his hand on my arm.

"You're under arrest, Dr. Waugh-hoo, alias Peters," says he, "for practising medicine without authority under the State law."

"Who are you?" I asks.

"I'll tell you who he is," says the Mayor, sitting up in bed. "He's a detective employed by the State Medical Society. He's been following you over five counties. He came to me yesterday and we fixed up this scheme to catch you. I guess you won't do any more doctoring around these parts, Mr. Fakir. What was it you said I had, Doc?" the Mayor laughs, "compound—well it wasn't softening of the brain, I guess, anyway."

"A detective," says I.

"Correct," says Biddle. "I'll have to turn you over to the sheriff."

"Let's see you do it," says I, and I grabs Biddle by the throat and half throws him out the window, but he pulls a gun and sticks it under my chin, and I stand still.

Then he puts handcuffs on me, and takes the money out of my pocket.

"I witness," says he, "that they're the same bills that you and I marked, Judge Banks. I'll turn them over to the sheriff when we get to his office, and he'll send you a receipt. They'll have to be used as evidence in the case."

"All right, Mr. Biddle," says the Mayor. "And now, Doc Waugh-hoo," he goes on, "why don't you demonstrate? Can't you pull the cork out of your magnetism with your teeth and hocus-pocus them handcuffs off?"

"Come on, officer," says I, dignified. "I may as well make the best of it." And then I turns to old Banks and rattles my chains.

"Mr. Mayor," says I, "the time will come soon when you'll believe that personal magnetism is a success. And you'll be sure that it succeeded in this case, too."

And I guess it did.

When we got nearly to the gate, I says: "We might meet somebody now, Andy. I reckon you better take 'em off, and—" Hey? Why, of course it was Andy Tucker. That was his scheme; and that's how we got the capital to go into business together.

DOROTHY PARKER (1893-)

. . . was using her remarkable talent at a very early age to write for the slickest magazines in New York. At 23, she was a drama critic for Vanity Fair; *at 27, she was a book reviewer for the* New Yorker.

Dorothy Parker achieved the unheard of when her first book of published verse became a best seller.

For her short story Big Blonde, *she won an* O. Henry Award. *Her writing, generally in a spare style, is marked by a bittersweet quality.*

When she cooed

YOU WERE PERFECTLY FINE

what game was she playing?

THE PALE YOUNG MAN eased himself carefully into the low chair, and rolled his head to the side, so that the cool chintz comforted his cheek and temple.

"Oh, dear," he said. "Oh, dear, oh, dear, oh, dear. Oh."

The clear-eyed girl, sitting light and erect on the couch, smiled brightly at him.

"Not feeling so well today?" she said.

"Oh, I'm great," he said. "Corking, I am. Know what time I got up? Four o'clock this afternoon, sharp. I kept trying to make it, and every time I took my head off the pillow, it would roll under the bed. This isn't my head I've got on now. I think this is something that used to belong to Walt Whitman. Oh, dear, oh, dear, oh, dear."

"Do you think maybe a drink would make you feel better?" she said.

"The hair of the mastiff that bit me?" he said. "Oh, no, thank you. Please never speak of anything like that again. I'm through. I'm all, all through. Look at that hand; steady as a humming-bird. Tell me, was I very terrible last night?"

"Oh, goodness," she said, "everybody was feeling pretty high. You were all right."

"Yeah," he said. "I must have been dandy. Is everybody sore at me?"

"Good heavens, no," she said. "Everyone thought you were terribly funny. Of course, Jim Pierson was a little stuffy, there for a minute at dinner. But people sort of held him back in his chair, and got him calmed down. I don't think anybody at the other tables noticed it at all. Hardly anybody."

"He was going to sock me?" he said. "Oh, Lord. What did I do to him?"

"Why, you didn't do a thing," she said. "You were perfectly fine. But you know how silly Jim gets, when he thinks anybody is making too much fuss over Elinor."

"Was I making a pass at Elinor?" he said. "Did I do that?"

"Of course you didn't," she said. "You were only fooling, that's all. She thought you were awfully amusing. She was having a marvelous time. She only got a little tiny bit annoyed just once, when you poured the clam-juice down her back."

"My God," he said. "Clam-juice down that back.
And every vertebra a little Cabot. Dear God. What'll
I ever do?"

"Oh, she'll be all right," she said. "Just send her
some flowers, or something. Don't worry about it. It
isn't anything."

"No, I won't worry," he said. "I haven't got a care
in the world. I'm sitting pretty. Oh, dear, oh, dear. Did
I do any other fascinating tricks at dinner?"

"You were fine," she said. "Don't be so foolish
about it. Everybody was crazy about you. The maître
d'hôtel was a little worried because you wouldn't stop
singing, but he really didn't mind. All he said was, he
was afraid they'd close the place again, if there was so
much noise. But he didn't care a bit, himself. I think he
loved seeing you have such a good time. Oh, you were
just singing away, there, for about an hour. It wasn't
so terribly loud, at all."

"So I sang," he said. "That must have been a treat.
I sang."

"Don't you remember?" she said. "You just sang one
song after another. Everybody in the place was listening. They loved it. Only you kept insisting that you
wanted to sing some song about some kind of fusiliers
or other, and everybody kept shushing you, and you'd
keep trying to start it again. You were wonderful. We
were all trying to make you stop singing for a minute,
and eat something, but you wouldn't hear of it. My,
you were funny."

"Didn't I eat any dinner?" he said.

"Oh, not a thing," she said. "Every time the waiter would offer you something, you'd give it right back to him, because you said that he was your long-lost brother, changed in the cradle by a gypsy band, and that anything you had was his. You had him simply roaring at you."

"I bet I did," he said. "I bet I was comical. Society's Pet, I must have been. And what happened then, after my overwhelming success with the waiter?"

"Why, nothing much," she said. "You took a sort of dislike to some old man with white hair, sitting across the room, because you didn't like his necktie and you wanted to tell him about it. But we got you out, before he got really mad."

"Oh, we got out," he said. "Did I walk?"

"Walk! Of course you did," she said. "You were absolutely all right. There was that nasty stretch of ice on the sidewalk, and you did sit down awfully hard, you poor dear. But good heavens, that might have happened to anybody."

"Oh, sure," he said. "Louisa Alcott or anybody. So I fell down on the sidewalk. That would explain what's the matter with my—Yes. I see. And then what, if you don't mind?"

"Ah, now, Peter!" she said. "You can't sit there and say you don't remember what happened after that! I did think that maybe you were just a little tight at dinner—oh, you were perfectly all right, and all that, but I did know you were feeling pretty gay. But you were so serious, from the time you fell down—I never knew you to be that way. Don't you know, how you told me I had never seen your real self before? Oh, Peter, I just couldn't bear it, if you didn't remember that lovely long ride we took together in the taxi! Please, you do remember that, don't you? I think it would simply kill me, if you didn't."

"Oh, yes," he said. "Riding in the taxi. Oh, yes, sure. Pretty long ride, hmm?"

"Round and round and round the park," she said. "Oh, and the trees were shining so in the moonlight. And you said you never knew before that you really had a soul."

"Yes," he said. "I said that. That was me."

"You said such lovely, lovely things," she said. "And I'd never known, all this time, how you had been feeling about me, and I'd never dared to let you see how I felt about you. And then last night—oh, Peter dear, I think that taxi ride was the most important thing that ever happened to us in our lives."

"Yes," he said. "I guess it must have been."

"And we're going to be so happy," she said. "Oh, I just want to tell everybody! But I don't know—I think maybe it would be sweeter to keep it all to ourselves."

"I think it would be," he said.

"Isn't it lovely?" she said.

"Yes," he said. "Great."

"Lovely!" she said.

"Look here," he said, "do you mind if I have a drink? I mean, just medicinally, you know. I'm off the stuff for life, so help me. But I think I feel a collapse coming on."

"Oh, I think it would do you good," she said. "You poor boy, it's a shame you feel so awful. I'll go make you a whisky and soda."

"Honestly," he said, "I don't see how you could ever want to speak to me again, after I made such a fool of myself, last night. I think I'd better go join a monastery in Tibet."

"You crazy idiot!" she said. "As if I could ever let you go away now! Stop talking like that. You were perfectly fine."

She jumped up from the couch, kissed him quickly on the forehead, and ran out of the room.

The pale young man looked after her and shook his head long and slowly, then dropped it in his damp and trembling hands.

"Oh, dear," he said. "Oh, dear, oh, dear, oh, dear."